THE LYLE ANTIQUES & THEIR VALUES

DOLLS & TOYS

Identification & Price Guide

COMPILED & EDITED BY
TONY CURTIS

While every care has been taken in the compiling of information contained in this volume the publishers cannot accept any liability for loss, financial or otherwise, incurred by reliance placed on the information herein.

The publishers wish to express their sincere thanks to the following for their involvement and assistance in the production of this volume:—

KAREN DOUGLASS
JANICE MONCRIEFF
ANNETTE CURTIS
TANYA FAIRBAIRN
SALLY DALGLIESH
FRANK BURRELL
ROBERT NISBET
LOUISE SIMPSON
JONN DUNLOP
EILEEN BURRELL

Printed in Denmark by ⊕ Nørhaven A/S, Viborg
ISBN 0-86248-108-2

INTRODUCTION

While this series of handy volumes has been specially devised to provide busy dealers and collectors with an extremely comprehensive reference library of antiques and their values, the information will also prove to be of great general interest to those with just a few pieces they wish to sell or appraise.

Each volume is crammed with over 2,000 detailed illustrations highlighting the distinguishing features of a broadly representative selection of specialised antiques and collectibles accompanied by descriptions and prices computed from recent auction figures.

We have endeavoured to obtain a balance between the more expensive collector's items and those which, although not in their true sense antiques, are handled daily by the antiques trade.

The illustrations and prices in the following sections have been arranged to make it easy for the reader to assess the period and value of all items with speed.

When dealing with the more popular trade pieces, in some instances a calculation of an average price has been estimated from the varying accounts researched.

As regards prices, when 'one of a pair' is given in the description the price quoted is for a pair and so that we can make maximum use of the available space it is generally considered that one illustration is sufficient. This will also apply when a description reads eg; part of a service, suite or a set.

It will be noted that in some descriptions taken directly from sales catalogues originating from many different countries, some terms are used in a broader sense than is customary, but in all cases the term used is self explanatory.

Pocket size with a sturdy binding, perfect for use in shops, flea markets and at auctions, *The Lyle Antiques and Their Values Identification and Price Guides* are your keys to smart antique buying or selling.

Tony Curtis

ACKNOWLEDGEMENTS

Abridge Auctions, (Michael Yewman) Market Place, Abridge, Essex RM4 1UA
Anderson & Garland, Anderson House, Market Street, Newcastle. NE1 6XA
Banks & Silvers, 66 Foregate Street, Worcester.
Barbers Fine Art Auctioneers, The Mayford Centre, Smarts Heath Road, Mayford, Woking.
Bearnes, Rainbow, Avenue Road, Torquay. TQ2 5TG
Biddle & Webb, Ladywood, Middleway, Birmingham. B16 0PP
Bloomsbury Book Auctions, 3 & 4 Hardwick Street, London.
Boardman Fine Art Auctioneers, Station Road Corner, Haverhill, Suffolk. CB9 0EY
Bonhams, Montpelier Galleries, Montpelier Street, Knightsbridge, London. SW7 1HH
Bracketts, 27-29 High Street, Tunbridge Wells, Kent. TN1 1UU
J. R. Bridgford & Sons, 1 Heyes Lane, Alderley Edge, Cheshire.
British Antique Exporters, 206 London Road, Burgess Hill, W. Sussex. RH15 9RX
Brogden & Co., 38 & 39 Silver Street, Lincoln.
Wm. H. Brown, Westgate Hall, Grantham, Lincs. NG31 6LT
Lawrence Butler & Co., Butler House, 86 High Street, Hythe, Kent. CT21 5AJ
Capes, Dunn & Co., The Auction Galleries, 38 Charles Street, Manchester. M1 7DB
Chancellors Hollingsworth, 31 High Street, Ascot, Berkshire. SL5 7HG
Christie's, 8 King Street, St. James's, London. SW1Y 6QT
Christie's, 502 Park Avenue, New York, N. Y. 10022
Christie's, Cornelis Schuystraat 57, 1071 JG, Amsterdam, Holland.
Christie's East, 219 East 67th Street, New York, N. Y. 10021
Christie's & Edminston's, 164-166 Bath Street, Glasgow.
Christie's S. Kensington Ltd., 85 Old Brompton Road, London. SW7 3LD
Coles, Knapp & Kennedy, Georgian Rooms, Ross-on-Wye, Herefordshire. HR9 5HL
Cooper Hirst, Goldway House, Parkway, Chelmsford. CM20 7PR
Dacre, Son & Hartley, 1-5 The Grove, Ilkley, Yorkshire.
Dee & Atkinson, The Exchange Saleroom, Driffield, N. Humberside. YO25 7LJ
Dickson, Davy & Markham, Elwes Street, Brigg, S. Humberside. DN20 8LB
Wm. Doyle Galleries Inc., 175 East 87th Street, New York.
Drewcutts, Donnington Priory, Donnington, Newbury, Berkshire.
Hy. Duke & Son, Fine Art Salerooms, Weymouth Avenue, Dorchester, Dorset. DT1 1DG
Elliott & Green, Auction Salerooms, Emsworth Road, Lymington, Hants, SO4 9ZE
R. H. Ellis & Sons, 44-46 High Street, Worthing, West Sussex. BN11 1LL
Farrant & Wightman, 2/3 Newport Street, Old Town, Swindon.
John D. Fleming & Co., 8 Fore Street, Dulverton, Somerset. TA22 9EX
Fox & Sons, 5 & 7 Salisbury Street, Fordinbridge, Hants. SP6 1AD
Geering & Colyer, 22-26 High Street, Tunbridge Wells. TN1 1XA
Rowland Gorringe, 15 North Street, Lewes, Sussex.
Goss & Crested China Ltd., N. J. Pine, 62 Murray Road, Horndean, Hants. PO8 9JL
Andrew Grant, 59-60 Foregate Street, Worcester.
Graves, Son & Pilcher, 71 Church Road, East Sussex. BN3 2GL
Giles Haywood, The Auction House, St. John's Road, Stourbridge, W. Midlands. DY8 1EW
Heathcote Ball & Co., The Old Rectory, Appleby Magna, Leicestershire.
Hobbs & Chambers, 'At the Sign of the Bell', Market Place, Cirencester, Gloucestershire. GL7 1QQ
Honiton Galleries, High Street, Honiton, Devon.
Edgar Horn, 46-50 South Street, Eastbourne, Sussex. BN21 4XB
Jacobs & Hunt, Lavant Street, Petersfield, Hampshire. GU32 3EF
W. H. Lane & Son, 64 Morrab Road, Penzance, Cornwall. TR18 2QT
Lawrence Fine Art, South Street, Crewkerne, Somerset. TA18 8AB
James & Lister Lea, 11 Newhall Street, Birmingham.
Locke & England, 18 Guy Street, Leamington Spa, Warwickshire. CV32 4DG
Thomas Love & Son, South St. John Street, Perth, Scotland.
R. J. Lucibell, 7 Fontayne Avenue, Rainham, Essex.
Mallams, 24 St. Michael's Street, Oxford.
May, Whetter & Grose, Cornubia Hall, Par, Cornwall.
Moore, Allen & Innocent, 33 Castle Street, Cirencester, Gloucestershire. GL7 1QD
Morphets, 4-6 Albert Street, Harrogate, Yorkshire. HG1 1JL
Neales of Nottingham, 192 Mansfield Road, Nottingham. NG1 3HX
D. M. Nesbit & Co., 7 Clarendon Road, Southsea, Hants. PO5 2ED
Onslows Auctioneers, 14-16 Carroun Road, London. SW8 1JT
Osmond, Tricks, Regent Street Auction Rooms, Clifton, Bristol, Avon. BS8 4HG
Outhwaite & Litherland, Kingsway Galleries, Fontenoy Street, Liverpool. L3 2BE
Phillips, The Old House, Station Road, Knowle, Solihull, W. Midlands. B93 0HT
Phillips Auctioneers, The Auction Rooms, 1 Old King Street, Bath, Avon. BA1 1DD
John H. Raby & Son, 21 St. Mary's Road, Bradford.
Reeds Rains, Trinity House, 114 Northenden Road, Sale, Manchester. M33 3HD
Russell, Baldwin & Bright, Ryelands Road, Leominster, Herefordshire. HR6 8JG
Sandoe, Luce Panes, Wotton Auction, Rooms, Wotton-under-Edge, Gloucestershire. GL12 7EB
Robert W. Skinner Inc., Bolton Gallery, Route 117, Bolton, Massachusetts.
H. Spencer & Sons Ltd., 20 The Square, Retford, Notts.
Stalker & Boos, 280 North Woodward Avenue, Birmingham, Michigan.
David Stanley Auctions, Stordan Grange, Osgathorpe, Leics. LE12 9SR
Street Jewellery Society, 10 Summerhill Terrace, Newcastle-upon-Tyne.
Stride & Son, Southdown House, St. John's Street, Chichester, Sussex.
G. E. Sworder & Sons, Chequers, 19 North Street, Bishops Stortford, Herts.
Theriault, P. O. Box 151 Annapolis, Maryland 21404.
Vidler & Co., Auction Offices, Cinque Ports At., Rye, Sussex.
Wallis & Wallis, West Street Auction Galleries, Lewes, Sussex. BN7 2NJ
Ward & Partners, 16 High Street, Hythe, Kent.
Warner, Wm. H, Brown, 16-18 Halford Street, Leicester. LE1 1JB
Warren & Wignall, 113 Towngate, Leyland, Lancashire.
Peter Wilson Fine Art Auctioneers, Victoria Gallery, Market Street, Nantwich. CW5 3DG
Wooley & Wallis, The Castle Auction Mart, Castle Street, Salisbury, Wiltshire. SP1 3SU
Eldon E. Worrall & Co., 15 Seel Street, Liverpool.
Worsfolds Auction Galleries, 40 Station Road West, Canterbury, Kent.

CONTENTS

DOLLS & TOYS

A French bisque head Paris-Bebe doll by Danel and Cie. £2,100

Mary period, circa 1690, recently appeared at auction. One, just over 12 inches high and still wearing her original saffron yellow gown, came up for sale at Phillips in London. This wonderful old doll was sold for the very high price of £24,000. The second doll from the same decade, wearing her original clothes and a wig of real auburn hair, was sold for £17,000.

Dolls dating from before the 17th century are extremely rare and between the 1600's and the late 1800's most of them were owned exclusively by rich society ladies who had them dressed in clothes of silk and satin in the fashions of the day. Dolls were considered to be too good for children who played with rough ones made of rags or carved wood and few of those have survived. It was the late 19th century before the practice began of giving pretty, well dressed dolls to little girls. Some of the best of those dolls were made in Germany or in France.

The child in all of us cannot but respond to the appeal of dolls and toys, especially those that take us back to our own childhood.

Any toy auction always has the expectant air of a long ago Christmas bazaar with the patrons ooh-ing and ah-ing over the items on offer. And no wonder for some of them are truly delightful — far too good to ever be played with as their pristine condition often proves.

For to fetch really high prices at auction, toys and dolls should be wearing their original clothes, should be still in their original boxes if possible and be unchipped and unscuffed. They must have spent their years wrapped in tissue paper at the back of some nursery cupboard, only to be taken out and handled very gently now and again as a special treat.

The imagined history of many of those toys is part of their fascination for collectors who must have let their imaginations run riot when two very rare dolls of the William and

A rare William and Mary wooden doll in original clothes, circa 1690. (Phillips) £24,000

6

'Answer-game', a Japanese battery operated robot with flashing eyes by Ichida, 1960's. (Christie's)   *£1,334*

like the Kammer & Reinhardt model which recently sold for £26,000. A pretty doll from the same manufacturer would probably cost around £500.

There are also collectors specialising in dolls of the '30's like the many Shirley Temple dolls which were made then. A composition portrait doll of the young film star made in Germany about 1934 sold recently for £242. Dating from the same time was a set of composition dolls representing the famous Dionne quins with a doctor and nurse which sold for £418. Walt Disney dolls were produced in large numbers during the 1930's also and a set of Chad Valley's Snow White and the Seven Dwarfs with cloth faces, blue glass eyes and velvet limbs, made £308 at auction. Four Disney figures of Mickey Mouse and Pluto with two Widgets in stuffed velveteen made £286.

Teddy bears are always eagerly sought after by collectors, especially if they were made by Steiff, the German manufacturers. The distinctive signs of a good Steiff bear are long arms, a distinct snout, a hump on its back and a button in its ear. If it meets all those criteria and if its plush is in good condition, the sky is the limit for its price. A black plush Steiff teddy bear with a shaved snout, elongated arms, a back hump and a button in its left ear recently fetched £3,220 at Phillips in London. Another brown plush bear by the German manufacturers Bing made £2,400. A more ordinary bear with only a slight hump and no button made £187.

The most famous names among the German makers were Armand Marseille, Lehmann, Simon and Halbig, and among the French, Schmitt and Jumeau. They all specialised in sweet faced bisque headed dolls with curled hair, glass eyes and jointed composition bodies. The prices paid today for those dolls would astonish the original purchasers because a Schmitt of Paris jointed bebe can make around £2,100 and one by Jumeau over £5,000. Strangely it is not the prettiest dolls that make top prices for they are often beaten by the plain Janes,

A Harlequin set of nine Steiff skittles, circa 1908, on circular wooden bases. (Lawrence Fine Art)   *£4,840*

Tin plate toys are a speciality field for many collectors who have pushed prices up to astonishing levels at times. Recently, at Christie's in Glasgow, an American collector bidding by telephone, paid £11,500 for a 39 inch long tin plate, clockwork, grey painted model of a First World War battleship by Marklin. A similar battleship dating from around 1910, which had been restored and repainted, made £450. The moral is not to tinker with toys. The original condition is always best.

A battery-operated four-door Cadillac State Service Car, boxed, 49cm. long. (Phillips) £220

The variety available in tinplate toys is immense, ranging from a Japanese tinplate clockwork model of a hen pulling a rickshaw (sold for £150) to a tinplate clockwork omnibus by Bing in maroon and cream, dating from around 1911, which made £8,500 at Phillips. The price was so high because it was in near mint condition. In New York an early Japanese keywind carousel of Donald Duck, made $5,000. Another wind up toy of "Paddy and the Pig" sold for £208 while a painted and lithographed tin wind-up sedan of the 1930's fetched £347. Even tinplate toys from the 1950's fetch premium prices like the Japanese clockwork robot "Lilliput" which sold for £280.

Karl Bub, clockwork Atom Rocket Ship, boxed. (Phillips) £110

A fine Marklin clockwork tinplate Nassau-class battleship, the motor driving three propellors, the hull painted brown and two-tone grey with simulated planked deck, in its original wooden crate bearing Marklin trade label, the model 39in. long. (Christie's) £10,500

8

A Royal Horse Artillery Gun Team in painted wood and composition by Sonnenberg, circa 1870. (Phillips) £3,600

A clockwork tin plate omnibus by Bing, circa 1911. (Phillips) £8,500

A Marklin hand painted tinplate Central Station, circa 1904. (Phillips, New York)
$19,000

Toy cars always make good prices, especially Dinky cars in their original boxes. Recently a boxed Dinky Weetabix van sold for £460 and a Gama tinplate 300 friction Cadillac in red and black, also with box, made £550. A Triang Minic pre-war Learner's car, boxed and with its key, made £300, while a French Jep painted tinplate Panhard Levassor, in tan with a red lining which was made around 1918, sold for £650. A 1910 German model of a four seater tourer, only just over 8 inches long, sold for £4,200.

Rocking horses range from the roughly carved 19th century model mounted on a wooden base with wheels which Christie's sold for £326 to the super Victorian dappled grey mounted on elegant rockers which fetched £1,945.

Antique dolls houses are bought today for high prices and dolls' house furniture, expecially pieces from the Victorian period, can go into very high prices. A typical suburban villa of the 1930's changes hands at around £500 if it is a dolls' house while earlier ones make even more. A large Victorian dolls' house with a hinged front section can sell for about £700 and the more ornate examples soar into the thousands. Like early dolls, the earliest dolls' houses were made as playthings for adults and they were furnished with articles of fine

An early hand enamelled four-seater open tourer, German, circa 1910, 8¼in. long. (Christie's) £4,200

10

woodwork and silver, with the walls decorated in handblocked wallpapers and silks. They originated in Germany and the earliest ones were imported from there as early as 1660.

A 70mm. scale figure of the Colonel-in-Chief, the Welsh Guards, with painted legend 'South Africa 1947' on the base, in original box, Britain's. (Phillips) £1,200

Other interesting toys include model theatres like the one which was illuminated by a candle mounted behind and which sold for £180, and a 1930's wind up tinplate gramophone painted with nursery figures which sold for £60.

Toy soldiers have always been in a class of their own as far as collecting is concerned and prices show no signs of dropping. A set of Royal Horse Artillery soldiers on horseback going at a gallop with officers and four mounted gunners, all in their original box and dating from about 1940, made £7,000 at Phillips in London and the same auction house scored a world record for a single toy soldier when they sold a scale figure of the Colonel in Chief of the Welsh Guards for £1,200. It was cast as a souvenir figure of Edward VIII when he was Prince of Wales but it had been over-painted with the legend 'South Africa 1947' and was marketed as a souvenir of King George VI's and Queen Elizabeth's visit to that country in 1947.

An early set of figures of the Royal Horse Artillery gun team during the Crimean War period, made by a German manufacturer, sold for £3,600.

The Royal Horse Artillery at the gallop in steel helmets by Britains. (Phillips) £7,000

Britains extremely rare display set 131, the largest set ever made by Britains, consisting of 281 figures including cavalrymen, infantrymen, bandsmen, sailors and Camel Corps soldiers, circa 1905. (Phillips) £10,000

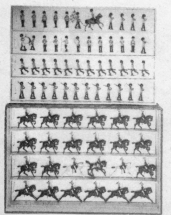

Large display box Set 93, containing Coldstream Guards with mounted officer, four pioneers, thirteen-piece band, two officers, twelve marching, twelve running, two trumpeters, six troopers and fifteen normal troopers, 1938, Britain's. (Phillips) £7,000

One of the great names of toy soldier production is William Britain who began making lead models around 1893 when the British Empire and national pride in military might was at its highest. Britain's produced models of every regiment in the British army and went on increasing their range until recent times.

Models fixed to a round base are more valuable than those on rectangular bases and anything stamped 'Made in England' dates from after 1937. Today most sets of lead soldiers can fetch at least £100 but the rarer ones go for considerably more. For example, a set of Salvation Army bandsmen sells for at least £1,000 and an early set of a Howitzer No 2 team with ten horsemen dragging a howitzer gun can make £900. The Britain's set of the band of the Coldstream Guards changes hands at around £2,000, but the world record price is for the extremely rare display set no 131, the largest set ever made by Britain's, consisting of 281 figures which recently sold for £10,000 at Phillips.

AMUSEMENT MACHINES

Jennings Tic-Tac-Toe
slot machine in chrome
case, 28in. high. £650

A large Football machine,
circa 1935, 64in. high.
£640

A Little Stockbroker
machine, circa 1935,
26in. high. £180

A six-sided Allwin Column,
circa 1925, 66½in. high.
£550

Caille 'The New Century'
Detroit five-cent upright
single-wheel slot machine,
circa 1900. £3,530

A Bryants All-Square
Merchantmen Crane in
stained oak casing, circa
1930, 84in. high. £420

American 'twenty-one' gambling
machine, circa 1930, 13½in.
wide. £80

An Art Deco style Mills 5c
coin operated slot machine.
£684

Coin operated mechanical
sweepstakes game, manu-
factured by RMC, trademark
Rock-Ola, circa 1930?, 12in.
high. £348

AMUSEMENT MACHINES

A 'Stars of the Silver Screen' machine, circa 1935, 27in. high. £352

Rare prohibition gambling machine with metal body, circa 1930, 6in. high. £143

Gottlieb & Co. 'World Fair' pinball table with glass top, 51in. long. £200

Caille gambling machine with five coin slots, circa 1910, 25½in. high. £200

An Aeroplane Allwin-type machine, circa 1940, 33in. high. £99

Coin operated mechanical football game, manufactured by The Baker Novelty Co., circa 1933, 17½in. high. £155

'Pussy' Shooter, coin-operated amusement machine by British Automatic Co. Ltd., circa 1935. £500

The French Execution Coin-slot Automaton, circa 1935, 84in. high. £495

AMUSEMENT MACHINES

'The Haunted House', coin-operated automaton, circa 1935, 70½in. high. £550

'Haunted Churchyard' automaton in mahogany case, circa 1912, 72in. high.£600

'The Night Watchman', coin-operated automaton by The British Automatic Co. Ltd., circa 1935, 66½in. high. £600

'Laughing Sailor', amusement machine, coin-operated bearing Ruffler & Walker plaque, 68½in. high, circa 1935. £650

'Haunted House' automaton in wooden case with glazed window, circa 1935, 70in. high. £300

Allwin 'Peerless de Luxe' with seven winning chutes, circa 1925, 29½in. high. £100

Mutoscope by the International Reel Co., circa 1905, 74in. high. £500

Brooklands Totalisator bandit with coin slot, circa 1939, 24in. high. £121

15

AMUSEMENT MACHINES

'Playball' Allwin with seven winning chutes, in oak case, circa 1920, 27½in. high. £100

'Test Your Strength' amusement machine with iron grip handle, circa 1925, 50in. high. £600

'Pussy' Shooter, amusement machine, circa 1935, 76in. high. £400

Ahrens stereoscopic viewer in oak cabinet, circa 1925, 68in. high. £750

American coin-operated mutoscope 'Death Dive', circa 1915, 50in. high. £500

Auto Stereoscope in oak casing with coin slot, circa 1930, 22½in. high. £225

Early Genco pinball bagatelle table with glass top, circa 1935, 39in. long. £450

White City 'Screen Stars' gambling machine in oak casing, circa 1940, 26½in. high. £100

AMUSEMENT MACHINES

'The Drunkard's Dream', coin-operated automaton, 66½in. high, circa 1935.   £600

'The Burglar', coin-operated automaton, circa 1935, 67in. high.   £400

Caillie Brothers grip-test amusement machine in green-painted case, circa 1910, 59in. high.   £750

'Great Race' game, coin-operated, in oak casing, 47in. wide, circa 1925.   £700

Ahrens '22-Man Football' game, coin-operated, in oak casing, circa 1930, 43¾in. wide. £650

Green Ray 'Television' amusement machine, circa 1945, 75in. high.   £250

Arhens 'Test Your Strength' amusement machine in painted wooden case, circa 1922, 79in. high.   £750

'Zodiac' coin-operated fortune-teller, circa 1940, 24½in. high.   £175

17

ANIMAL TOYS

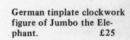

A Lehmann Performing Sea Lion, No. 445, in original cardboard box, German, circa 1900, 7½in. long. £165

A 'Peter Rabbit' chickmobile, hand car, No. 1103, circa 1935. £424

German tinplate clockwork figure of Jumbo the Elephant. £25

Part of a collection of five tinplate toys, comprising two prancing horses, a steam engine, a circular saw bench and another item. £10

Monkey on a string by Lehmann, 6in. long. £40

A painted tinplate cat, 'Nina', EPL No. 790, by Lehmann, circa 1907, 11in. long. £1,000

French early 20th century Decamps chamois-covered walking pig, 15in. long. £572

A pair of models of Tyrannosaurus Rex and Triceratops. £130

An English leaping clockwork hare. £45

ANIMAL TOYS

An unusual Decamps walking
terrier, French, circa 1900,
12in. long.   £242

A clockwork German cow finished
in brown and cream, the mechanism causing the animal to walk
and nod, 18.5cm. long.   £100

19th century papier-mache
elephant with glass eyes,
18in. long.   £255

Early 20th century clock-
work musical trained golden
mohair bear, Germany,
7¼in. high.   £114

The Three Bears, a set of miniature
all bisque teddy bears jointed at
shoulder and hip wearing original
crochet clothes, 2¼in.-1¼in. high.
                         £385

A small German clockwork
leaping Kangaroo.   £45

19th century bisque and papier-
mache novelty, 13in. high.£885

A large Steiff rocking elephant,
45in. long, German, circa 1925.
                         £440

A plush covered lion cub, 9in.
long, circa 1925 with Steiff
button.   £88

A mid 19th century German portable barrel organ automaton, 52cm. wide.   £6,000

A French musical clock diorama, signed Hy Marc, 37¾ x 26¼in.   £1,550

A clockwork cabbage automaton containing a white rabbit, French, circa 1900, 6½in. high.   £297

A French weight-drive mechanical carte-de-visite/strip cartoon automaton, case 91½in. wide.   £350

A coin-operated monkey pianist automaton, with the mechanism contained in the oak base, probably French, late 19th century, 16in. high.   £3,000

Late 19th century French landscape automaton on ebonised base, 22in. high.   £440

Late 19th century German Boy on Swing automaton, 44in. high.   £605

A picture automaton, the timepiece in the church facade activates the clockwork mechanism, probably French, 35in. long.   £770

A Pussy Band Printed Paper automaton, circa 1910, 18in. high.   £290

AUTOMATONS
CONJUROR/MAGICIANS

An advertising display automaton on oak base, circa 1930, 25in. wide.   £880

A musical conjuror automaton by Lambert, the bisque head impressed (Depose Tete Jumeau 4), overall height 19½in. French, circa 1880.   £2,500

A 19th century bisque-headed Magicienne automaton.   £5,500

Automaton magician, 52½in. high, 36½in. wide.   £1,000

A musical conjuror automaton, probably Decamps, French 1880, overall height 17in.   £5,000

A musical conjuror automaton standing at her magic box, French, circa 1880, 18in. high by 12in. wide.   £4,000

A lady conjuror automaton, lavishly dressed in pink silk, mounted on square plinth, probably French, circa 1905, 26in. high.   £2,500

A musical automaton of a conjuror, probably by L. Lambert, French, circa 1880, 16in. high.   £1,430

Swiss automaton music box, circa 1900, of a magician, 23in. high.   £3,000

21

AUTOMATONS
DOLLS

French/German bisque automaton, doll by Simon & Halbig, circa 1890. 21in. high.   £3,820

An S.F.B.J. bisque doll and ball automaton, circa 1910, French, height 13in.   £500

A Leopold Lambert musical automaton doll, 'The Flower Seller', the Jumeau bisque head impressed 4, 19½in. high.   £3,500

A musical automaton, the bisque head impressed (Depose Tete Jumeau Bte. S.G.D.G. 4), French, late 19th century, height 20in.   £2,500

A clockwork wheeled toy of a bisque swivel headed ballerina of Parisienne type, French, circa 1880, 17in. high.   £1,320

A musical automaton by Lambert, in pale green silk dress and shoes, French, 1885, height 19½in.   £4,000

A bisque headed automaton with Armand Marseille head, probably German, circa 1900, 14½in. high.   £187

A cane birdcage automaton with bisque doll, German, circa 1915, overall size 13in.   £1,000

French musical automaton, the bisque head stamped Depose Tete Jumeau Bte. S.G.D.G.4, circa 1880, 18in. high.   £3,000

AUTOMATONS DOLLS

French type bisque auto-
maton, 18in. high, circa
1890.   £955

French bisque automaton doll,
in original blue taffeta gown,
circa 1880, height 19in.
                       £6,000

A French Bebe automaton
in original silk dress and
underclothes, early 20th
century.   £2,500

German bisque auto-
maton 'The Imhof
Walking Doll', 1898-
1909, 12in. high, with
key-wind mechanism.
                       £500

French musical automa-
ton of a girl seated smell-
ing flowers, by Leopold
Lambert, circa 1880,
19¾in. high.   £1,650

French bisque automaton
by Leopold Lambert,
circa 1900, 20in. high.
                       £1,595

French ballerina automaton
with bisque head impressed
S.F.B.J. 801, Paris, circa
1900.   £2,500

A crying Jumeau musical
automaton by Lambert,
the bisque head impressed
211 and (Depose Tete
Jumeau 4) French, circa
1890, height 20½in.
                       £2,500

A bisque headed automaton,
the German head impressed
5/0, probably French, circa
1900, 18in. high.   £462

AUTOMATONS
DOLLS

A musical automaton of a doll cradling her baby, probably German, circa 1890, 23in. high. £500

A musical automaton of a bisque headed doll beside a dressing table, marked Simon & Halbig S & H 6, the doll 15in. high. £2,000

A 19th century French automaton figure, head stamped Depose Tete Jumeau, 47cm. high. £2,500

A 19th century clockwork lady knitting automaton, Germany, 21in. high. £1,250

French bisque automaton by Emile Jumeau, circa 1890, 19in. high overall. £2,140

Early 20th century mother rocking baby automaton, German, the oak base contains the mechanism. £424

A bisque-headed automaton standing figure modelled as a child, 20in. high, the key marked L.B.4. £1,750

A sleeping doll automaton, the doll lying in a brass bedstead, probably French, circa 1910, 14in. £1,500

French bisque automaton fashion doll, probably Vicky, circa 1875, 15in. high. £1,500

AUTOMATONS
GROUPS

A musical automaton of a dancing couple by Vichy, French, circa 1860, 13½in. high. £1,320

A clockwork automaton toy of a bisque headed doll pulling a wooden two-wheeled cart with driver, 13in. long. £1,300

A French automaton dancing couple by Theroude, on velvet lined circular base, 12in. high. £950

Two Schoenau & Hoffmeister automaton dolls dressed as Pulchinelles, German, late 19th century, 21in. high by 12½in. £1,750

A hand-operated automaton of a garden tea party, German late 19th century, approx. 12½in. high by 11½in. wide. £3,000

Dancing negress automaton with key wound mechanism, in good condition, 10½in. high. £350

Late 19th century French clockwork musical automaton of two dancing figures, 13½in. high. £4,500

German automaton with bisque dolls, circa 1890, 26in. wide, with ten mechanical actions. £5,745

German bisque automaton, dolls by Armand Marseille, circa 1890, 12in. high. £635

AUTOMATONS
MALE FIGURES

An Armand Marseille musical/dancing bisque headed puppet doll, impressed 70·20,5. £525

19th century wooden and papier-mache automaton, 36in. high. £665

Mid 19th century papier mache two-faced clockwork musical automaton figure, 18in. high. £420

A composition headed automaton modelled as a standing Chinese man, 30in. high, French 1880. £6,000

An automaton figure of a clown with painted composition face and black and white costume, 18in. high, with glass dome. £1,430

Rare drinking musical automaton, probably by Vichy, circa 1890, slightly damaged, 29½in. high. £6,000

A papier mache automaton of a clown, the head inset with fixed blue glass eyes, 18in. high. £570

French bisque automaton, probably Farkas, circa 1920, 12in. high. £530

Late 19th century 'Boy Feeding Pig' automaton, the bisque head marked Jumeau SGDG 4, 18¾in. high. £1,805

rench musical automaton
iano player, head impres-
ed SFBJ 301 Paris, circa
910, 13in. high. £330

German early violinist and
harpist tinplate automa-
ton, circa 1895, 9¾in.
£500

French musical automa-
ton of a piano player,
circa 1915. £1,100

A German 19th century
automaton of an organ
grinder with miniature
dancers, on a garden stage.
£2,500

An automaton of a young girl
seated at an upright piano, the
French bisque head marked 4,
41cm. high. £3,000

A musical monkey harpist
automaton, probably by
Vichy, French, circa 1870,
19in. high. £4,500

A barrel organ grinder
automaton, probably
French, circa 1900,
17in. high. £385

A German musical auto-
maton, 'Musical Troupe'
with seven bisque dolls,
circa 1880, dolls 7in.
high. £2,000

An automaton mandolin
player, with musical movement in base, stamped G.
Vichy, Paris, 25½in. high.
£1,500

A gilt metal and enamel singing bird box, decorated with Watteauesque scenes. £750

Late 19th century singing bird music box, Switzerland, with bird-shaped key, 4in. wide. £1,500

Late 19th century French key-wind singing bird automaton, 4in. wide. £420

A 19th century square section bird cage of wire and turned wood, the base containing a musical box, 17in. high. £140

A singing bird automaton with clock, Swiss, probably by Jacquet Droz, circa 1785, 20in. high. £30,703

An early Issmayer small tinplate singing bird in cage, circa 1904, 8in. high. £300

A gilt metal and composition bird-cage containing a feathered bird automaton on a perch, 12½in. high. £770

Mid 19th century Swiss musical automaton of singing birds, 38in. high. £571

A 19th century European singing bird automaton, 22in. high. £1,115

A German silver and enamel singing bird box, struck with English import hallmarks for 1926, 4in. long. £1,885

Late 19th century Continental singing bird automaton in repousse sterling silver gilt casket, 4¼in. wide. £520

Early 20th century enamel singing bird automaton, 3¼in. high. £762

A French 19th century 'Penny in the Slot' singing bird in gilt cage automaton, 23½in. high. £1,500

Mid 19th century Swiss musical automaton of singing birds, on oval base, 60cm. high. £1,381

A Bontems singing bird automaton with three birds under a cage, French, mid 19th century, 21½in. high. £7,500

Mid 19th century Swiss gilt metal automaton with three singing birds, 21in. high. £1,885

A 19th century chased brass cased rectangular musical box with a hinged cover revealing a singing bird, 4.25in. long. £300

A Swiss or German singing bird cage with two articulated feathered birds, 52cm. high. £750

Spot-On — 156 Mulliner
Luxery Bus (pale blue/
silver), (M), boxed.
£420

Gunthermann, post-war
tramcar finished in orange,
cream and pale yellow.
£80

Gunthermann (W. Germany)
tinplate tram, circa 1930,
300mm. long. £130

Tootsietoy Greyhound Bus (U.S.A.),
diecast, circa 1940. £35

Triang (Great Britain), prewar tinplate
bus with white rubber wheels. £40

Johillco (Great Britain)
diecast double decker,
circa 1935. £85

Johillco (Great Britain)
diecast tram, circa 1935.
£120

Chad Valley (Great Britain),
single deck Midland Red
tinplate bus, 1930's. £200

Chad Valley (Great Britain), double
decker tinplate bus, 1949. £60

A Gunthermann tinplate and clockwork tramcar, No. 21, 25cm. long. £176

SES

French diecast Dinky toy,
Chausson, circa 1956.
£40

French Dinky toy,
diecast, Paris Soma,
circa 1951.   £50

French diecast Dinky toy,
Renault Isobloc, circa 1950.
£75

French tinplate trolleybuses by Joustra, circa 1951. Value £90 to £125.

Tippco (German) tinplate clockwork
streamline coach, circa 1950.   £45

Rico (Spain) tramcar with cut out
tin figures in the windows, circa
1910.   £200

Siku (W. Germany) one
and a half deck coach,
circa 1950.   £46

Siku (W. Germany)
Bussing coach,
circa 1950.   £35

Siku (W. Germany)
Riveria coach,
circa 1950.   £27

Trailways Greyhound Eagle, Made in Japan, 1960's tinplates.   £15 – £40

Tinplate coaches by Jaj, Portugal, circa 1960.   £15 – £20

Three plastic Dinky copies of the 1960's, by Maks, Hong Kong.   £8 – £10

Tinplate coaches by Joustra, France, one 1950's – £65, the other 1960's – £35.

Three small double deck, by Charbens, U.K., 1955 and 1958.   £25 — £30

CIJ Renault coach, diecast, 1953 — £35, a trolley, 1960 and a Solido coach, diecast.
£18 — £35

Tinplate San Francisco trams, Made in Japan, 1950's/1970's.   £15 — £20

Two double decks and trolleybus, by Wells Brimtoys, U.K., 1950's. £30 — £45

Wells Brimtoy (Great Britain) tinplate buses and coaches, circa 1950.
Value £30 to £60

Tootsietoy Greyhound Bus (U.S.A.), diecast, circa 1940.   £35

Chad Valley (Great Britain) double decker Greenline tinplate bus, circa 1930.   £250

Triang (Great Britain) prewar and postwar Greenline tinplate coaches.
Value £40 to £70

Copy of a Dinky toy one and a half deck coach by Maruson (Japan), 1950's. £85

Milton Morgan (India) copy of a Dinky coach, 1950's.   £20

1920's fretwork model of a bus.
£200

Wells Brimtoy Greenline tinplate
coach, 1950's.   £50

All Metal Toy Co. (U.S.A.), tinplate
coaches, 1940's.   £40

Betall tinplate
trolleybus,
circa 1950,
220mm. long.
£60

Betall (Great Britain)
tinplate trolleybus,
1950's, 175mm. long.
£40

Gunthermann (W. Germany)
tinplate General Bus, 1920's.
£300

Guinness tinplate bottle crate, 1964.
£60

C.I.J. (France) postwar
Renault coach.   £40

C.I.J. (France)
prewar Renault
coach.   £60

BUSES

A trolleybus, by C.R., France, 1950.   £50

A pre-war tinplate bus with white rubber wheels, by Triang, U.K.   £40

Tinplate coach, by Gunthermann, Germany, map on base, 1948.   £60

Large Bedford coach, by Fun Ho, New Zealand, cast aluminium, 1965.   £18

Guy Arab coach, by Mettoy, U.K. (predecessors of Corgie Toys), diecast, 1950.   £45

Mulliner Coach, by Spot-On, U.K., 1963. £15

Greenline tinplate coach, by Wells Brimtoys, U.K., 1950's.   £50

A Commer Avenger coach, by Chad Valley U.K., 1954.   £60

A double deck, by Chad Valley, U.K., 1949.
£85

A tramcar, No. 846, by Gunthermann, Germany, 1955.
£65

German Penny toys, 1930's.   £40

Minic Motorways double decker and coach, by Triang, U.K., 1960's.
£18 — £35

A 1950 tinplate Express bus, by Wolverine, U.S.A.
£60

A diecast trolleybus, by Taylor & Barrett, U.K., 1936.
£40

Jitney Bus, Made in Phillipines, 1970's/80's.
£15

Six-wheeled trolleybus, by Joustra, France, tinplate, battery operated lights, 1952. £95

BUSES

A printed tinplate model of a Green Line bus, German, circa 1925, 11½in. long.   £360

Cast Iron model of a Leyland Lion single decker bus   £750

A handbuilt working model of a 'Freelance' open topped tram.   £300

A J.E.P. tinplate Paris Bus, lithographed 'Madeleine . . .', French, circa 1925, 10¼in. long.   £330

Bing, English market clockwork tramcar of 'O' gauge proportions, 18.5cm. long.   £440

Spot-On — 145 L.T. Route-master Bus (transfer Radiator), (M), boxed.   £380

A Gunthermann tinplate and clockwork six-wheeled general double-decker bus, 35cm. long.   £165

A Gunthermann double-decker bus clockwork activated, German, circa 1930. £308

A rare Marklin clockwork four-seat Tourer, German, circa 1909, 9¼in. long.   £5,720

An unusual Marklin small limousine, German, circa 1900, 8¼in. long.   £2,420

A Carette lithographed tinplate and clockwork rear entrance four-seater Tonneau automobile, 12¼in. long, German, circa 1907.   £2,200

A Bing hand-painted open-cab limousine with bevelled glass windows, German, circa 1908, 10½in. long.   £2,310

A live-steam spirit-fired, hand enamelled model of a horseless carriage, probably by Bing, circa 1902, 9in. long.   £1,000

A Carette tinplate Open Tourer, German, circa 1906, 8in. long, together with original cardboard box.   £3,520

A Bing hand-enamelled tinplate model of a De Dion runabout motor car, circa 1905, 7½in. long.   £650

A German hand-painted Bing limousine, circa 1908, 8in.   £1,045

A printed tinplate model of a 1910 Daimler Voyage limousine, by Carette, 15½in. long.
£800

A Bing tinplate and clockwork limousine, 9¾in. long, circa 1910.
£1,870

Cast-iron early taxi cab, roofed open driver section,.enclosed cab section, circa 1910, 6in. long.
£60

A printed tinplate model of a 1910 Daimler Voyage limousine, by Carette, circa 1910, 15½in. long.
£2,200

A Bing tinplate De Dion vehicle, the clockwork mechanism driving the rear axle, 6in. long, German, circa 1910.
£550

A printed tinplate model of a limousine, by Carette, circa 1910, 15½in. long.
£1,400

A Gunthermann tinplate four-seat open tourer and passengers, German, circa 1910, 7½in. long.
£2,420

A Carette lithographed limousine, complete with driver, German, circa 1910, 8½in. long.
£1,430

A Bing hand-enamelled Mercedes type open tourer, circa 1912, 15¾in. long.   £4,800

A Moko clockwork six-cylinder saloon, 9½in. long, German, circa 1918-20.   £400

A Gunthermann painted and lithographed four-door limousine with clockwork mechanism, German, circa 1910, 11½in. long.£800

A Carette hand-painted four-seat Open Tourer, German, circa 1910, 12½in. long, together with original cardboard box.£7,000

A Carette tinplate and clockwork limousine, circa 1910.   £1,430

A Carette lithograph limousine, with clockwork mechanism, German, circa 1911, 8½in. long.   £720

Tinplate clockwork limousine and driver, 15in. long.   £1,250

A painted and lithographed German tinplate toy car, 4in. high.   £300

CARS, 1920-1929

A printed tinplate model of a limousine, by Tipp, circa 1920, 15in. long.
£350

An early Bing hand-painted open four-seat Tourer, German, circa 1920, 12¼in. long.
£3,000

A Bub tinplate and clockwork roadster, with tinplate driver, 36cm. long overall.
£1,230

The Buddy 'L', a painted metal push-along model T Ford Coupe, 10½in. long, U.S.A., circa 1924.
£308

A printed and painted tinplate model of a four-door limousine with clockwork mechanism, by Tipp & Co., circa 1928, 8¼in. long.
£480

Gunthermann Fire Car, German, circa 1925, 6¾in. long.
£500

A J.E.P. tinplate Renault Open Tourer, French, circa 1929, 13¼in. long.
£900

Turner steel four door sedan, circa 1924, 26½in. long.
£682

A Lehmann 'Gala' tinplate limousine, German, circa 1930, 12½in.   £600

A Marx Charlie McCarthy & Mortimer Snerd auto, 1939, lithographed tin, 16in. long.
          £385

A Bing lithographed open tourer, the clockwork mechanism driving the rear axle, 12½in. long, German, circa 1930.   £220

A Daimler Sedanca motor car, in the original box.   £320

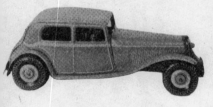

Mettoy, a large four-door Saloon finished in bright lime-green with cream lining, the interior with chauffeur at the wheel, in box, 35cm. long.   £80

Painted and lithographed tin wind-up sedan, circa 1930, 11½in. long.   £347

Fischer tinplate saloon finished in red and black, German, circa 1935, 12½in. long.   £600

A large and impressive Karl Bub tinplate and clockwork limousine, circa 1932, German, 50cm. long.   £968

CARS, 1930-1939

A Meccano non-constructional car, finished in red and blue, circa 1935, 8¾in. long.
£530

A tinplate limousine by Karl Bub, 14¼in. long, circa 1930.
£400

Pre-war tinplate model of a two-seater tourer car, 9½in. long, and a cardboard model of a 'Daily Mail' pre-war aircraft.
£30

An Ingap four-door limousine with clockwork mechanism, driving rear axle and operating front head lamps, 11¼in. long, circa 1930.
£385

Meccano, No. 2 Constructor Car constructed as a tourer, boxed.
£1,200

A Meccano car constructor kit, complete with clockwork model.
£750

A late 1930's toy sports coupe car with red roof and wings and gold wheels.
£700

A Triang Minic pre-war taxi (M), boxed, with key.
£350

A battery-operated four-door Cadillac
State Service Car, boxed, 49cm. long.
£220

A tin toy car, modelled as two-seater Model
A with leather wheels and painted details,
6in. high, 6in. wide, 20in. long.   £86

A German clockwork flying car, 19.5cm.,
and a Hungarian open tourer in blue, 26cm.
£70

'Cadillac', a printed and painted tinplate car,
with friction-drive mechanism, rubber tyred
wheels and tinted windows, by Ichiko, circa
1967, 28in. long.   £395

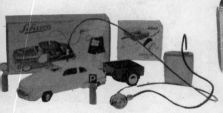

A Schuco Ingenico electric remote control
car 5311/56, and a Carreto 5330 trailer, in
original boxes.   £209

Gama tinplate 300 friction Cadillac in red
and black, (M), boxed, 31cm. long. £550

Spot-On, set No. 260, The Royal Presentation
Set, in original box.   £209

French C.I.J. tinplate Fregate Panhard,
French, circa 1955, 12½in. long.   £150

CARS, 1940-1970

Solido XJ12's, now ceased production.
£5 — £10

Dinky Toys, SS100 Jaguar, produced 1946-50.
£15 — £25

Spot-On Mark X with turning wheel and opening boot, 1963-64.   £15 — £30

Dinky Toys, XK120 model, produced 1954-62.
£15 — £25

Corgi Toys, Mark X with opening boot and bonnet, 1962-67.   £10

Corgi Toys, XJ Coupe, with opening doors and bonnet.   £4

Corgi Toys, E type with racer in the foreground, production car behind, 1962-64. £15 — £25

Corgi Toys, Jaguar XJS racer with good detail, current model.   £3.50

Corgi Toys, MK1 Jaguar, in yellow trim, 1960-63. £15 — £25

Dinky Toys, XJ Coupe B roadspeed, limited production in the 1970's, no box issued. £3 — £5

Western Models, D types, (No. 6 Hawthorns 1955 Le Mans Winner). £15 — £25

Western Models, MK11, 3.8 Jaguar, current model. £26

Burago SS100, well detailed current model showing engine components, exhaust and suspension. £10

Matchbox Series, 3.8 MK11, complete with original box, 1959-67. £5 — £10

Dinky Toys D type Jaguar in light green, complete with original box, 1957-62. £15 — £30

Matchbox Model of yesteryear, SS100, current model. £3

Spot-On — 'A' Presentation Set T1, comprising
Bentley Saloon, Consul Classic, Triumph TR3,
Isetta, Austin A40.   £130

A Marklin Racing Car Set, comprising two
cars, drivers, track, layout, transformer and
instructions, German, circa 1935.   £500

A boxed set of diecast Build-Yourself
vehicles, by Solido.   £45

Corgi, Gift Set No. 23, Chipperfields Circus
Models, in original presentation box. £264

Spot-On — 2A Presentation Set. £750

Spot-On — Presentation Pack of four Sports
Cars (E to M), boxed.   £220

Spot-On cars, including No. 256 Jaguar
Police car, two No. 215 blue Daimler SP 250
and No. 191/1 Sunbeam Alpine Hardtop,
all in original boxes.   £143

CHILDREN'S BOOKS

'The Mystery of the Spiteful Letters', Enid Blyton, 1949.   £3.50

'Horace and the B.B.C.', by Harry Hemsley.   £15

'Alice in Wonderland', Pears Illustrations. £3

'The Book of Soldiers', E. P. Dutton & Co. £12   'Run-Away Dick', by Harry Eliott, 1936. £6.50

'Some Farm Friends', circa 1900.   £10

'Little Wide Awake 1890'. £25

'Merry Hearts 1896'. £35

CHILDREN'S BOOKS

'Under One Flag', Tuck, circa 1900. £3.50

'The House That Jack Built', George Routledge & Sons. £20

'The Girl's Own Annual 1934'. £15

'The Book of the Teddy Bear', 1964. £10

'Ameliaranne Camps Out', 1st Edition, 1939. £15

CHILDREN'S BOOKS

'From Many Lands, America', Father
Tuck Series, 1904.   £15

'The Birds' Alphabet', 1946. £4.50

'Our Darlings', circa 1910. £12

'The Tom Merry's Own', 1950.
£4.50

'The Alphabet Book', 1880's. £15

'The Beano Book', D. C.
Thompson.   £12

'The Dandy Monster Comic',
1948.   £25

'The Beano Book', 1968.
£6.50

'Girls' Crystal Annual 1953'.
£3.50

'Billy Bunter's Own'.   £4

'The Jolly Gnomes Annual',
1951.   £10

'Teddy Tail's Annual', 1939.
£5.50

'The Companion Annual',
1924.   £3.50

'Okay Adventure Annual',
Boardman & Co.   £6

CHILDREN'S BOOKS

'The Felix Annual', 1930's. £12

'Eagle Annual Number One', 1952. £12

'More Adventures of Rupert', Daily Express 1947. £35

'Knockout Fun Book', 1955. £8

'The Schoolgirls' Own Annual 1923. No. 1'. £10

'News and Chronicle Boys' & Birls' Annual', by Enid Blyton. £6

'Nursery Fun', Dean's Picture Book. £1

'Mrs Tickler's Caravan', Cecil Aldin, 1931. £15

'Lucie Attwell's Annual.' £7

'The Frog Prince', M. L. Atwell Illustrations, 1920's.   £10

'The Little Ebony Elephant', by Fitz.   £3.50

'The Adventures of Old Man Coyote', 1945.   £1.50

Bubbles, Volume 7.   £18

'The Willie Waddle Book', 1930's.   £15

The Magic Doorway.   £8

'The Brave Little Tailor', 1923.   £12

'Swift Annual', 1962. £2

'The Ship of Adventure', Enid Blyton, 1st Edition, 1950.   £12

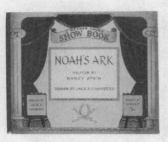

'Bunter Keeps It Dark', 1960, 1st Edition.   £6

'Noah's Ark', Peepshow Book, by Nancy Spain.   £3.50

'The Adventures of Larry the Lamb', 1940's.   £5

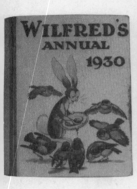

Wilfred's Annual 1930.
                                    £16

Peter Pan and Wendy — illustrated by Mabel Lucie Attwell.   £25

Arabian Nights — illustrated by A. E. Jackson.   £15

'The Gorilla Hunters', by R. M. Ballantyne.   £1.50

'Easy A B C Book', circa 1850. £8

'The Quest for the Perfect Planet', W. E. Johns, 1961.
                                    £4

Treasure Island 1929 —
illustrated by Rowland
Hilder. £10

Pip and Squeak Annual 1931.
£20

My Favourite Annual 1933.
£8

Greyfriars Holiday Annual
1921. £20

Rover Book for Boys 1940.
£10

'Blown to Bits', by R. M.
Ballantyne, 1889. £3

Chatterbox 1907. £7

Peggy and Joan — illustrated
by Honor Appleton. £9

The Oojah Annual. £6

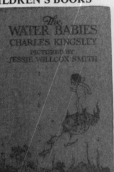

ater Babies 1938 — illustra-
d by Jessie Wilcox Smith.
£22

My Book of Ships 1913.
£5

Armchair Story Book 1937.
£8

'Teddy Tail of the Daily
Mail', £8

'Jill the Reckless', Eighth
Printing, 1928. £1.50

'The Splendid Savage', by
Conrad H. Sayce. £2

Big Book of Mother Goose,
has revolving disc of hunt
scene in cover. £12

Playbox Annual 1918.
£16

Golden Annual for Girls
1925. £7

57

CHILDREN'S BOOKS

'Children's Outdoor Games', by G.
B. Crozier, 1910.   £6.50

'My ABC of Nursery Rhyme Friends', Tuck
circa 1940.   £8

'The Animal ABC', Deans Diploma Series No. 28. £7

'Radio Fun Annual', 1957.
£7

'ABC for Little Willie', Daily News Ltd. £7.50

CLOCKWORK TOYS

early French mechanical tri-list, circa 1890, 8¼in. long. £770

An early painted tinplate fish, with clockwork mechanism causing the fish to flap its fin, 8¼in. long, by Bing, circa 1910. £220

Lehmann tin wind-up 'Li La', Germany, circa 1903, 5½in. high. £347

oy tin elephant, riding a cooter and balancing an bject on it's trunk, mar-ed 'U.S. Zone, Germany', irca 1950's. £20

Goodwin clockwork doll and carriage, doll with papier mache head, 11in. high, 9½in. long, 1868. £682

A toy tin 'balancing ball' elephant, marked 'U.S. Zone Germany', 1950's. £35

New Century Cycle', EPL 345, with clockwork mecha-nism, by Lehmann, circa 1910, 5in. long. £850

Lithographed tin Toonerville Trolley, New York, 1922, 6½in. high. £450

Linemar, battery operated Bubble Blowing Popeye. £240

CLOCKWORK TOYS

Lehmann 'Naughty Boy' tin wind-up toy, 1904-35, 4.5/8in. long. £190

A rare tin plate beetle by Lehmann, Germany, which walks and flaps its wings. £90

George W. Brown clockwor doll pushing hoop bell toy, Connecticut, 1872, 12in. long. £3,000

A 20th century wind-up toy, French celluloid spherical artist, 4in. high, and a Japanese mohair pup in basket, 6in. high. £76

A Doll & Co. printed and painted carousel with a handcranked clockwork mechanism, 11½in. long, circa 1914. £308

An early Lehmann, EPL marque 'Paddy riding his pig to market', with clockwork mechanism, circa 1910, 5½in. long. £320

Dummy cigar box in which a hand and head pop out when a concealed button is pressed. £25

Unique Art tin wind-up Li'l Abner and his Dogpatch Band, America, 1946, 8½in. high. £250

A. G. Vichy bisque-headed tri-cyclist automaton, French, circa 1880, 10½in. long. £495

CLOCKWORK TOYS

An English J.W.B. mechanical artist toy, contained in original box, circa 1900, 4½in. wide. £770

Lehmann 'Zig-Zag' tin wind-up toy, 1910-45, 5in. long. £381

A tinplate mechanical lobster, German, circa 1910, 8½in. wide. £352

'The Juba Dancers', carved and stained wood mechanical toy, by Ives, U.S.A., circa 1874, 10in. high. £286

Late 19th century Connecticut clockwork dancing black couple, 10½in. high. £1,770

A painted tinplate toy of a monkey on a four-wheel musical carriage, German, circa 1903, 7½in. long. £280

Lehmann 'Paddy and the Pig' tin wind-up toy, 1903-35, 5½in. long. £208

A Lehmann 'Lo and Li' tinplate toy. £1,040

Early 19th century rooster squeak toy, moulded papier mache body on coiled wire legs, 5in. high. £133

CLOCKWORK TOYS

A hand-painted tinplate model of a walking pigeon, possibly French, circa 1910, 7½in. long. **£85**

'Popeye the Sailor', No. 268, a printed and painted tinplate toy of the cartoon sailor in a rowing boat, 14in. long, by the Hoge Mfg. Co., Inc., U.S.A., circa 1935. **£1,300**

A Lehmann tinplate Anxious Bride, No. 470, German, circa 1910. **£495**

A Lehmann Mikado Family, No. 350, German, circa 1898, 6½in. long. **£550**

A Gunda-Werke lithograph tinplate motorcycle and sidecar with clockwork mechanism, 6½in. long, circa 1920, and a tinplate monkey moneybox. **£825**

'Echo', EPL 725, an early printed and painted tinplate motorcyclist with clockwork mechanism operating a metal painted spoked wheel, by Lehmann, circa 1910, 8¾in. long. **£1,760**

A Lehmann Africa, No. 170, flywheel-driven ostrich cart, German, circa 1900, 7in. long. **£308**

A Lehmann 'Kadi' tinplate toy, No. 723, German, circa 1920, 7in. long. **£418**

CLOCKWORK TOYS

A mechanical walking crocodile, possibly by Decamps, 34in. long, French, circa 1915.   £550

Marx wind-up 'Bunny Express' train, circa 1920.   £480

'Mac 700', a printed and painted tinplate motorbike and rider with clockwork mechanism, causing the rider to hop on and off, 7¼in. long, by Arnold, W. Germany, circa 1955.   £286

French 'Le Faucheur' scythe man by F. Martin, circa 1900, 7½in. high.   £418

A German post-war clockwork Boxing Match, boxed (no lid).   £70

'Bulky Mule, The Stubborn Donkey', EPL No. 425, by Lehmann, circa 1910, 7½in. long. $217 £150

Marx tin wind-up Moon Mullins and Kayo Handcar, America, 1920's, 5½in. high.   £233

A merry-go-round with a wheel driven mechanism.   £200

A painted tinplate toy of a cooper, by F. Martin, Paris, circa 1902, 7½in. long. £660

A Hull & Stafford-type tinplate hoop toy, the horses with clockwork mechanism between, American, circa 1871, 9in. diam. £880

Late 19th century painted tin clockwork bowing man 7½in. high. £115

A Lehmann tinplate 'Oh My', No. 690, the articulated figure holding the clockwork mechanism, circa 1920, 10½in. high. £400

A tinplate 'Rudy' walking ostrich, the underside marked 'Nifty', 8½in. high, German, circa 1925. £132

American composition character automaton, circa 1880, 21in. high. £300

German clockwork automaton of a Chinese mandarin pulling a cart, circa 1900, man impressed Halbig. £1,100

A painted toy of a skater, with clockwork mechanism, by A. F. Martin, French, circa 1890, 8½in. high. £700

An early printed and painted tinplate automobile, 'Tut Tut EPL No. 490, by Lehmann, circa 1910, 6¾in. long. £900

OCKWORK TOYS

aker and Sweep', E.P.L. No. 0, by Lehmann, circa 1905, original box. **£1,600**

A German clockwork Drummer Boy dressed as a soldier in busby, 28cm. high. **£65**

Early 20th century lithographed tin wind-up toy, Japanese 'Chick-Chick', 10in. long. **£150**

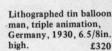

unthermann wind-up painted tin merry-go-round, ermany, 1920's and 1930's, 0in. high, 10.3/8in. diam. **£1,040**

Marx, clockwork Hi-Yo-The Lone Ranger, boxed. **£90**

Lithographed tin balloon man, triple animation, Germany, 1930, 6.5/8in. high. **£320**

Nurnberger Blechspielwarenfabric, lockwork novelty toy in the form f a circus elephant with roller ball hute, 1950, 24cm. high. **£70**

Late 19th century Martin clockwork drunkard, 8in. high. **£75**

Lehmann, early flywheel driven 'Africa', EP2 No. 170. **£250**

DISNEYANA

Unusual tinplate and composition Minnie Mouse and pram, probably by Wells, 7½in. long, circa 1933. £1,500

'The Three Caballeros', an original Walt Disney celluloid, signed, 18 x 16in., framed and glazed. £1,750

'Mickey Mouse Organ Grinder', tinplate toy with clockwork and musical mechanisms, by Distler, circa 1930, 6in. long. £650

Marx tin wind-up Merry Makers, 1930, 9in. high. £200

Marx, Walt Disney's Donald Duck Duet, boxed. £240

Pelham Puppets, Mickey Mouse and Minnie Mouse. £60

Seven Walt Disney opaque glass ornaments, circa 1935, 4½in. to 7in. £750

DISNEYANA

'Jiminy Cricket', original Walt Disney celluloid, framed and glazed, 16¼ x 17½in. £500

Back and front of German tinplate Mickey Mouse mechanical bank, circa 1930, 6¾in. high. £450

Pinocchio doll, with clock-work movement within the articulated legs, circa 1942, 7½in. high. £300

'The Mickey Mouse Fire Brigade, 1936'. £35

Pinocchio doll by Ideal Novelty & Toy Co., 7¼in., circa 1945. £250

American Mickey and Minnie Mouse, plaster painted models, 9in. high, circa 1945. £150

'The Moles', a celluloid taken from 'Song of the South', framed and glazed, 12¼ x 10½in. £150

DISNEYANA

One of two original hand paintings on celluloid, from the Walt Disney film Snow White and the Seven Dwarfs, 6½ x 9½in. £650

Alarm clock, clockface depicting the Three Little Pigs, circa 1935, 6in. high. £250

Lead model Mickey and Minnie Mouse barrel organ group. £38

Mickey Mouse, stuffed toy by Dean's Rag Book Ltd., circa 1930, 6¼in. high. £250

Walt Disney's Pinocchio, 1940. £12

'Minnie Mouse', stuffed to by Dean's Rag Book Ltd., circa 1930, 7in. high. £200

'Felix the Cat', large plush-covered toy with cloth bow tie, 28½in. high, circa 1930. £850

Four Disney stuffed figures, comprising a velveteen Mickey Mouse and Pluto; two corduroy 'Widgets', late 1930's-40's. £286

Glazed earthenware musi cal jug depicting the 'Three Little Pigs', circa 1935, 10in. high. £200

NEYANA

erican Mickey and Minnie Mouse, two Fune-
x painted wooden toys, circa 1931, 6¾in.
h. £250

Walt Disney's 'Alice in Wonderland' Punch-Out Book, 1955. £15

lt Disney rug in tufted cotton, showing
aracters from his films, 1950's, 104 x 70in.
£300

'he Three Caballeros', three plaster figures of
isney characters, circa 1950. £150

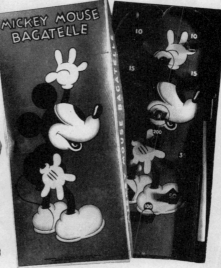

Mickey Mouse Bagatelle by Chad Valley Co. Ltd. £30

Early 19th century English composition articulated toy modelled as an old woman, 13in. high.   £380

A bisque headed doll, C1912, by Franz Schmidt, 12½in. high.   £310

A musical jester doll which bangs its cymbals and plays a tune when its tummy is pressed.   £60

A Scottish boy doll in Highland dress, with bisque head, in original box marked 'Kelly Boy 306', 12in. high.   £110

Pair of cloth character dolls, made by Norah Wellings, England, circa 1930, each 11in. high.   £245

19th century all china doll in one piece, circa 1885, 12in. high.   £2

Pedigree Coronation doll in original clothes, 14in. high.   £22

An Edwardian 'Austrian' porcelain doll with fixed eyes, 8½in. high.   £100

A bisque shoulder headed doll with fixed blue eyes, marked Goss 18, 17in. high £40

isque-headed charac-
child doll with brown
ping eyes, 24in. high.
£500

Rabery and Delphieu bisque
doll with jointed body, in
ivory satin dress, 28in. high.
£325

A bisque shoulder headed
doll with closed mouth,
solid pate and kid body
with bisque arms, 14½in.
high. £352

painted cloth character doll
th blue shaded eyes, ginger
ool wig and jointed legs, 18in.
gh, with Deans Rag Book Co.
d. circa 1926. £200

A pair of advertising dolls
modelled as the 'Bisto Kids',
designed by Will Owen, 11in.
high, circa 1948. £209

A bisque headed character
baby doll moulded as an
Oriental, 9¼in. high,
marked 3/0. £418

bisque headed doll with
nted complexion and kid
overed body, 21in. high.
£250

A bisque two-faced doll with
original blonde wig and with
jointed composition body,
11in. high. £900

A bisque headed autoperi-
patetikos doll with painted
blue eyes and brown kid
arms, 10in. high. £200

DOLLS

19th century porcelain
doll, circa 1850, 17in.
high, in green silk gown.
£390

Early 20th century ventrilo-
quist's dummy in a military
coat.   £200

A pink china should
headed doll, the kid
body with wooden
limbs, 15in. high, ci
1840.   £3

An 18th century group of Italian creche figures, six average height 9in., four average
height 11½in., and two at 14½in.
£2,242

A bisque headed bebe with
papier mache jointed body,
marked 12 by Steiner, 29in.
high.   £2,400

English cloth character
doll, by Dean's Rag Book
Co. Ltd., of Lupino Lane,
13in. high.   £206

A cloth doll painted in oils
with grey eyes and blonde
painted short hair, 23in. high
£200

OLLS

white bisque-headed
own doll with fixed blue
ves, marked 157 3, 11in.
igh.   £250

A bisque shoulder headed
doll, the stuffed body with
bisque limbs, 11½in. high,
circa 1860.   £715

A bisque-headed clock-
work walking talking doll,
14in. high.   £350

A bisque headed character doll with a quantity of other items, including bedding, shoes,
a parasol, a box of washing items and twenty-three changes of clothes, 14½in. high,
marked F.S. and Co., 1272/352 Deponiert.   £935

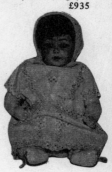

A large Lencidschango
Oriental cloth doll, 23in.
high, circa 1925, together
with a late 19th century
Chinese silk tunic. £440

A composition character headed
doll modelled as Lord Kitchener,
in original clothes with Sam
Browne hat and puttees, 19in.
high.   £164

A Franz Schmidt bebe doll
with sleeping brown eyes,
open mouth and composition
body, 9in. high.   £125

A bisque-headed child doll, label reading Gekleidete Puppe no. 9052, circa 1880. £750

A bisque shoulder headed doll with brown sleeping eyes, marked 309,5, 17in. high. £200

A painted cloth doll made for Oxo Ltd. by Deans Rag book Co. Ltd., 17in. high. £300

A china doll of an Irish gentleman, with gusseted kid body and china lower limbs, 13in. high. £120

A bisque headed child doll with auburn wig and jointed composition body, 32in. high. £400

A 19th century porcelain doll with slight pink tinted complexion, 14in. high. £150

A composition headed Japanese doll with closed mouth, inset eyes and black hair wig, 16½in. high. £165

A terracotta headed creche figure modelled as a Turk with moustache and pigtail, painted wooden hands and feet, 19in. high. £330

19th century porcelain doll with black moulded hair, 12in. high. £530

DOLLS
AMERICAN CHARACTER

American composition child doll, with mohair wig, circa 1940, 21in. high. £175

American composition personality doll by the Reliable Toy Co., circa 1935, 17in. high. £200

American plastic character doll with bendable knees, circa 1965, 7½in. high. £400

American wooden character doll of Felix, by Schoenhut, 9in. high. £350

An autoperipatetikos cloth-headed doll, stamped Patented July 1862: also Europe 20 Dec. 1862, American, circa 1862, 9in. high. £350

American composition character doll of Jimminy Cricket, by the Knicker-bocker Toy Co., circa 1935, 10in. high. £160

American artist all bisque doll in one piece by Jeanne Orsini, New York, 1920, 7in. high. £450

American plaster character Buddha-like figure, by Rose O'Neill, 5½in. high. £30

American plastic character doll, with soft head, circa 1962, 12in. high. £200

DOLLS
AMERICAN CHARACTER

American composition character doll, produced by Cameo, circa 1926, 17in. high.   £270

American cloth character doll by Charlene Kinser, 25in. high.   £70

American artist all bisque doll 'Miss Muffet', 1981, on purple tuffet, 7in. high   £150

American cloth child doll, New York, circa 1900, 22in. high.   £450

Pair of American composition character dolls by Pat Burnell, 1976, 14in. high.   £100

A composition shoulder headed doll, by Joel Ellis or the Cooperative Doll Co., 11in. high.   £198

American plastic character doll, by Terri Lee, circa 1965, 16in. high.   £155

American plastic lady doll, New York, circa 1975, 21in. high.   £450

American wooden character doll of Mr Peanut, 8in. high.   £70

OLLS
MERICAN CHARACTER

American composition character doll of Shirley Temple, circa 1935, 13in. high. £280

American composition character doll, 14in. high, circa 1940, in original clothes. £250

American cloth character doll, by Marjorie H. Buell, circa 1944, 14in. high. £245

American composition character doll by Effanbee, circa 1940, 17in. high, dressed in formal wear. £350

Late 19th century American cloth Folk Art doll, 23in. high in original plaid dress. £250

Composition child doll by the American Doll Co., New York, circa 1940, in riding clothes, 13in. high. £350

American composition character doll of Pinocchio made by Ideal Novelty & Toy Co., circa 1935, 12in. high. £140

American composition character doll 'Bobbie-Mae', circa 1940, 12in. high, in original box. £200

American artist all bisque doll 'Little Bo Peep', 1981, 10in. high. £225

DOLLS
AMERICAN CHARACTER

American cloth child
doll, styling indicative
of Art Fabric Mills,
circa 1895, 13in. high.
£200

American plastic Lissy-
faced character doll,
circa late 1950's, 12in.
high.   £400

A painted cloth charact
doll with jointed velvet
body, 17in. high.   £25

American composition
character doll of Aunt
Jemima, by Tony Sarg,
circa 1925, 18in. high.
£350

American composition
character baby, contained
in its original cardboard
trunk, 10in. high. £200

American cloth charact
doll, made by Georgene
Novelties Inc., circa 194
13in. high.   £25

A painted cloth Lenci-
type doll wearing original
Red Indian costume, 16in.
high.   £350

American papier-mache
and plush character doll,
circa 1909, 13in. high.
£200

American compositio
character doll of Mort
mer Snerd, circa 1940
13in. high.   £350

OLLS
MERICAN INDIAN

Southwestern polychrome male figure, Yuma, attached card reads 'Bought 1892 Albuquerque, New Mexico', 8¾in. high.   £475

Hopi polychrome wood Kachina doll, 'Bule Mana', early 20th century, 13in. high.   £561

Hopi polychrome wood Kachina doll, 'Ang-ak-China', early 20th century, 9in. high.   £238

Hopi polychrome wood Kachina doll, possibly the clown figure, 'Piptuka', early 20th century, 8½in. high.   £505

Late 19th century Hopi polychrome wood Kachina doll, possibly 'Qoia', a Navajo singer, 16½in. high.   £2,247

Yuma polychromed female figure with traditional horsehair coiffure, inscribed 'Yuma, Arizona Indian 1931', 8in. high.   £255

Plains polychrome and fringed hide doll, Northern, 1880's, 18½in. high. £1,011

A Hopi wood Kachina doll, 'Mahuu' (locust), with black, mustard and rose decoration over a white painted body, 15¾in. high.   £816

Plains beaded and fringed hide doll, Northern, 1880's, 13½in. high.   £898

DOLLS
ARMAND MARSEILLE

Armand Marseille doll, fully jointed body and limbs, clothed and in glazed wooden case. **£150**

German bisque character doll, by Armand Marseille, circa 1920, 24in. high. **£431**

An Armand Marseille shoulder-bisque Marotte doll, German head for French body, circa 1900 15in. high. **£750**

A bisque headed doll with jointed composition body, marked Armand Marseille, Germany A9M, 24in. high. **£190**

Pair of Armand Marseille bisque headed dolls. **£300**

Bisque character doll by Armand Marseille, circa 1920, 7in. high, in original Dutch costume. **£400**

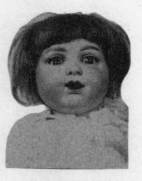

Early 20th century Armand Marseille bisque headed Floradora doll, 14in. high. **£130**

An Armand Marseille '980' bisque headed doll with open and shut eyes, dressed, 22in. high. **£180**

German bisque character doll with five-piece papier mache body, by Armand Marseille, circa 1925, 7in. high. **£280**

DOLLS
ARMAND MARSEILLE

A bisque headed doll with moving eyes, marked on head A.M. 4DEP, Made in Germany, 19in. high. £180

German bisque child doll wearing an original Shaker costume, by Armand Marseille, circa 1925, 16in. high. £208

Bisque headed character doll by Armand Marseille, circa 1920, 12in. high, in excellent condition. £750

An Armand Marseille bisque-headed 'dollie', wood and composition ball jointed body, 24in. high. £170

German bisque child doll with composition and wooden ball jointed brown body, by Armand Marseille, circa 1895, 13in. high. £312

A brown bisque-headed baby doll with brown composition baby's body, 14½in. high, marked AM341/2.5K. £220

A bisque headed character child doll, marked 231 DRMR 248 FANY A2/0M, 14in. high. £2,420

A bisque-headed character baby doll, marked AM353/4K, 17in. high. £900

German bisque headed character doll, Fany by Armand Marseille, circa 1915, 14in. high. £3,000

DOLLS
BRU

A bisque shoulder headed fashion doll, possibly by Bru, French, circa 1880, 12in. high. **£990**

A Bru Teteur bisque doll, French, circa 1875, 19in. high. **£4,400**

French Bru Jeune bisque doll in original silk dress and bonnet, 16½in. high, circa 1875. **£4,00**

A 'walking/crying' Bru Jeune R bisque doll, French, circa 1895, 24½in. high, in original Bebe Bru Marchant No. 9 box. **£3,300**

A bisque headed bebe with jointed wood and composition body, marked BRU Jner 4, 13in. high. **£1,800**

A bisque headed clockwork walking, talking bebe petit pas, marked BRU Jne R 11, 24in. high. **£2,500**

A bisque headed bebe with five upper teeth, fixed brown eyes and pierced ears, 18½in. high. **£800**

A bisque-headed bebe, the fixed wrist jointed composition body dressed in blue, impressed SteA.1, 16in. high. **£1,870**

French bisque child doll, marked Bru Jne R9, says 'Mama' when legs move, 1895. **£2,420**

A set of Chad Valley Snow White and the seven dwarfs. Snow White with painted cloth
face, fixed blue glass eyes and velvet limbs, 17in. high, the dwarfs in original clothes,
9½in. high. £308

English cloth character
doll with velvet head,
probably Chad Valley,
circa 1935, 20in. high.
£175

A Chad Valley painted felt portrait
doll modelled as the Princess Elizabeth,
circa 1938, 18in. high. £308

English cloth character doll
by Chad Valley, 18in. high,
with mohair plaited wig.
£450

A 'Chad Valley' boxed set of Snow White and the Seven Dwarfs in Original clothes, Snow
White with painted pressed felt face, jointed velvet body, the blue velvet bodice with
pale blue and pink slashed sleeves and short cape, 17in. high, the Dwarfs 9½in. high.
£2,860

DOLLS
DOLL'S HOUSE DOLLS

A bisque headed doll's house doll modelled as a man with a black-painted moustache and hair, 7in. high. £132

A pair of all bisque doll's house dolls modelled as roguish girls, jointed at neck, shoulder and hip, 3½in. high. £462

A bisque headed doll's house doll modelled as a man, 6½in. high. £198

A bisque headed child doll with closed mouth, fixed blue eyes, blonde wig and composition body, 7in. high, marked 16. £110

An all bisque doll's house doll, marked 253 12 on the head and body, 5¼in. high, and an all bisque standing character boy, 3¼in. high. £99

A bisque headed doll jointed at neck, shoulder, thigh and knee, 7in. high, marked 199 2/0, also a doll's house doll, 5in. high. £165

A bisque headed doll's house doll modelled as a man with full beard and hair, 6½in. high. £209

Two all bisque doll's house dolls with fixed blue eyes, blonde wigs and moulded socks and shoes in original national costume, 4in. high. £110

A bisque headed doll's house doll modelled as a man with cloth body and bisque hands, 6in. high. £143

Simonne bisque shoulder-
eaded fashion doll, French,
rca 1870, 17½in. high.
£1,980

French bisque character doll
with mohair wig, by A. Marque,
early 20th century, 22in. high.
£25,000

French bisque child doll,
by E. Denamur, circa
1885, 11in. high.   £635

Unusual French bisque
doll, circa 1870, 17in.
high, in original shot-
silk dress.   £400

Large French bisque bride doll
with kid body, 26½in. high,
circa 1875.   £3,000

French bisque doll with
jointed wood and com-
position body, circa
1895, 21½in. high.
£350

Rare French shoulder bisque
Oriental doll in original
clothes, circa 1860, 13in.
high.   £5,000

A French mechanical
walking doll, the bisque
head with blonde mohair
wig, 38cm. high.   £680

An F. Martin 'Le Gai
Violiniste', in original
clothes, French, circa
1920, 7¾in. high.
£240

DOLLS
FRENCH

A French bisque shoulder-
headed fashion doll with a
kid-covered wooden body,
45cm. high.   £3,000

French cloth character doll,
by Poupees Gerbs, circa
1924, 28in. high.   £173

French bisque child do
circa 1875, 20in. high.
          £1,5

A black bisque doll impressed 34-24, with jointed
wood and composition
body in original pink dress,
probably French, circa
1910, 14¼in. high. £1,320

A French bisque headed doll
with cork pate, the leather
shoes impressed with a number 11, a bee and a Paris
Depose, 25in. high.   £1,350

A swivel-head shoulder-
bisque doll, with kid body
French, circa 1860, 13in.
high, together with a crear
chintz bag, circa 1880.
                    £825

French all bisque minia-
ture doll, circa 1880,
in 'Jester' costume, 6in.
high.   £400

A bisque headed Pulchin-
elle puppet, impressed 2,
French, circa 1870, 24in.
high.   £1,210

A swivel headed clockwor
musical walking doll, with
a Parisienne type head,
21in. high.   £1,000

ench FG bisque fashion
ll in original blue dress,
in. high circa 1875.
£1,000

A swivel-head bisque doll,
French, circa 1850, 15½in.
high.   £770

French plastic figure doll,
signed Maurice Milliere,
circa 1920, 16in. high.
£300

rench bisque lady doll,
erdinand Gaultier's
arisienne with Gesland
ockinette body, circa
870, 23in. high.
£2,065

French bisque lady doll
with wooden articulated
body, circa 1870, 31in.
high.   £3,855

French bisque lady doll,
circa 1870, 19in. high,
with kid and wooden body,
£1,500

A bisque-headed bebe, the
ointed body dressed in pink,
9in. high, marked on the
ead 8 and with the Schmitt
f Paris shield mark on
ottom.   £2,090

Pair of French bisque adult
dolls by Ferdinand Gaultier
circa 1890, 13in. high.
£1,000

French bisque child doll
with blonde human hair
wig, marked 137, 14in.
high.   £694

DOLLS
FRENCH

A Marotte shoulder-bis-
que doll, probably
French, circa 1900, 14in.
high.   **£400**

A bisque-headed bebe
with closed mouth, mar-
ked E. J. A 10, 1878
Paris, 25in. high.
£5,000

A bisque-headed bebe,
with string pulls for voi
box marked Jullien 10,
24½in. high.   **£1,600**

French bisque lady doll,
circa 1875, 18in. high,
with wooden body.
£2,000

A bisque figure of a seated naked
woman with moulded black
bobbed hair, 3in. high.   **£99**

French bisque child
doll, circa 1870, in
original muslin dres
and bonnet, 13in.
high.   **£450**

Japanese bisque character
doll, with French type composition and wooden join-
ted body, circa 1910, 13in.
high.   **£240**

A Dep Tete Jumeau bisque
headed doll, impressed DEP
8, with jointed wood and
composition body, 19in.
high.   **£350**

French bisque child doll,
marked Mon Cheri, by Lar
ternier Et Cie, circa 1915,
18in. high.   **£280**

▶rench bisque child
▶oll, circa 1880, in
▶riginal dress and bon-
▶et, 9½in. high.
£550

Rare negro bisque doll, probably
French, circa 1870-85, 16in.
high.   £2,500

A china-headed autoperi-
patetikos with moulded
black ringlets, 10½in.
high.   £400

▶ench bisque fashion doll,
▶ca 1860, with kid torso,
▶in. high.   £945

Pair of French bisque shell
dolls, probably by F. Gaultier,
circa 1875, 10½in. high.
£1,490

French bisque novelty doll,
torso forming sweet con-
tainer, 18in. high, circa
1890.   £750

A wax-headed figure of a
fashionable woman, in-
scribed Lafitte Monsieur,
1910, 14in. high.   £50

French bisque headed
child doll, circa 1935,
11½in. high.   £400

A wax figure of a fashionable woman, marked
Lafitte Desinat, 1915,
12in. high.   £75

DOLLS
GERMAN

A bisque headed character baby doll with open closed mouth, marked 211 J.D.K., 17in. high.   £380

Bisque headed German doll marked 'Mignon', 22in. high.   £275

German all bisque character doll of Kewpie, Rose O'Neill fantasy creature, circa 1910, 11in. high.   £275

German all bisque figure doll, circa 1915, 18½in. high.   £700

Two German all bisque miniature dolls, 5in. high, circa 1900, with mohair wigs.   £300

Huret bisque doll with socketed head and jointed body circa 1860, 17½in. high.   £7,500

A shoulder-bisque doll with fixed blue glass eyes, German, circa 1890, 17in. high.   £264

Rohmer china head doll with wooden joints, circa 1866, 14in. high.   £2,000

German bisque child doll with wooden body, circa 1915, 18in. high.   £75

A bisque-headed character
boy doll, impressed 7
3072 and with JDK sticker
on the body, 20in. high.
£605

German all bisque
novelty doll, circa
1900, 2¼in. high.
£150

German porcelain half doll of an
adult nude woman, by Dressel
& Kister, circa 1910, 6in. high.
£763

German black papier-
mache doll with fixed
black enamel eyes,
circa 1860, 7½in. high.
£330

Set of six late 19th century all bisque dolls,
German, mounted in candy box, inscribed
on cover 'found in the nursery of a ruined
old chateau — Verdun, France — 1917',
4in. high.   £393

German celluloid character
doll, wearing original outfit,
marked Kecsa, 16in. high.
£120

A German bisque head doll,
marked 283/297, Max Hand-
werck, 24¾in. high.   £260

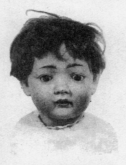

A bisque headed character
baby doll, marked K & W
13, Konig and Wernicke,
24in. high.   £380

A shoulder-china doll, the
long face with painted features, German, circa 1860,
15½in. high.   £400

91

DOLLS
GERMAN

A German Marotte doll, the circular wood body containing the musical mechanism, circa 1890, 12in. high.   £300

German Motschmann-type waxed composition doll lying in a basket, circa 1860, 9in. long.
£300

German all bisque character doll, circa 1915, 3½in. high.   £150

Heubach Koppelsdorf bisque headed doll, 20½in. high.
£220

A German porcelain half doll, 'Pierrette', circa 1920, 9½in. high.   £750

Late 19th century Heubach 12-Koppelsdoft bisque headed doll, impressed AWW, German 32in. high.   £568

German porcelain half doll with painted facial features, circa 1910.
£150

Early 20th century German bisque bathing belle, resting on one hand, the other raised shielding her eyes, 3½in. high.   £330

German porcelain character figure, circa 1920, 14in. high.   £250

A German bisque charac-
ter doll with toddler body
and 'tremble' tongue,
circa 1915, 30in. high.
£2,250

German bisque headed
character baby doll,
circa 1925, 10in. high.
£400

A bisque-headed charac-
ter baby doll with brown
sleeping eyes, marked
JDK 257, 17½in. high.
£350

German porcelain half
doll, by Dressel & Kister,
circa 1920, 5in. high.
£300

A German bisque head doll,
marked Heubach-Koppelsdorf,
250-4, 25¾in. high.　　£260

German bisque half doll,
incised marks suggest
Mettlach production,
circa 1910, 4in. tall.
£400

A composition headed
Motschmann type baby doll
with dark inset eyes, painted
curls and floating hands and
feet, 8in. high, circa 1850.
£418

Early 20th century German
bisque bathing belle with
painted facial feature and
auburn wig held in a net cap,
3in. high.　　£264

A bisque shoulder-headed
doll, possibly by Steiner,
having a Motschmann-type
body, 29cm. high.　£550

German bisque Oriental
doll with five-piece com-
position body, circa
1910, 10½in. high.
£450

Late 19th century German
bisque headed novelty doll,
13in. high.   £325

German bisque headed doll
with original blue knitted
frock and hat, 13in. high.
£680

A large shoulder-papier-
mache doll with kid body
and wooden lower limbs,
German, circa 1830, 24in.
high.   £660

Two dolls, one impressed
with a clover leaf 5, the
other W.D. 5, with fixed
brown glass paperweight
eyes, German, circa 1900,
13½in. high.   £880

German bisque character
doll, the wooden ball-
jointed body with 'walker'
mechanism, circa 1910,
27in. high.   £820

German bisque miniature
doll, circa 1920, with
papier-mache body, 6½in.
high.   £200

German bisque character
doll with blonde mohair
wig, the kid body label-
led 'Dainty Dorothy',
circa 1911, 25in. high.
£550

A large shoulder-china doll
with kid body in original
dress, German, circa 1860,
20in. high.   £175

German porcelain half doll, by Dressel & Kister, circa 900, 6in. high. £190

A roly-poly Santa, Germany, probably early 20th century, 10in. high. £115

German bisque novelty figure of a young boy, circa 1910, 3½in. high. £100

bisque headed doll with composition body, marked orzellan Fabrik Burggrub aslachende Baby, 1930/3/ lade in Germany DRGM, 8in. high. £430

Four German all bisque character dolls, depicting characters from 'Our Gang', 2in. to 3½in. high, together with a book, 1929. £104

A Bahr & Proschild bisque doll, impressed B & P 320.12 de, in white broderie-anglaise dress, German, circa 1885, 21in. high. £990

German bisque character doll with brown moulded hair, circa 1920, 13in. high. £2,500

A Hebe bisque headed doll, marks indistinct, with open mouth and upper teeth, sleeping blue eyes and long fair plaited hair, 24in. high. £187

A china-headed doll, the cardboard and stuffed body with squeaker and china lower limbs, German, circa 1860, 15in. high. £880

DOLLS
GOOGLIE EYED

A composition mask faced googlie eyed doll, with smiling watermelon mouth, wearing spotted dress, 10½in. high. £330

A bisque headed character baby doll with blue intaglio googly eyes, marked C93?52 6/0M, 9in. high. £400

A composition mask faced googlie eyed doll, with smiling watermelon mouth, wearing pinafore and bonnet, 9in. high. £187

German bisque character doll with 'googly' eyes, by Strobel & Wilkens, 12in. high.£1,750

A bisque group of two googly-eyed figures in original hats, by William Goebel, 3½in. high. £308

An all-bisque googly-eyed doll's house doll with smiling water-melon closed mouth, 4in. high. £220

GRODENTHAL

A painted wooden Grodenthal type doll with grey curls, circa 1835, 12½in. high. £550

German early Grodenthal peg-wooden doll, circa 1820, 9¼in. high. £200

An early Grodenthal type painted wooden doll with brown eyes, circa 1820, 18in. high. £1,400

rman bisque character doll by
ubach, circa 1915, 9in. high,
th 'googly eyes'. **£450**

Pair of German all bisque
novelty dolls, possibly by
Gebruder Heubach, circa
1900, 4in. high. **£175**

A bisque figure of a seated
fat baby, marked 95 and the
Heubach square mark, stamped in green 68, 5in. high,
together with two child dolls.
£99

bisque figure of a chubby baby, impressed
o. 9902, 4½in. high, and a bisque figure of
baby playing with his toes, 5½in. long,
mpressed Gebruder Heubach. **£385**

Trio, German all bisque miniatures, by Gebruder
Heubach, circa 1900, each about 5in. high.
£500

rman bisque character doll by
ubach, circa 1915, 10in. high.
£400

A bisque-headed whistling
doll, marked with the
square Heubach mark,
11½in. high. **£525**

German bisque character doll with
papier-mache body, 8in. high, by
Heubach, circa 1915. **£200**

DOLLS
JUMEAU

A Henri Lioret phonograph Jumeau doll, impressed 11, French, circa 1893, 25in. high. £1,870

An Emile Jumeau bisque 'talking' doll, circa 1880, 19in. high, together with clothing. £5,000

A fine French bisque head doll by Emile Jumeau, circa 1885, 15in. high. £1,50

A bisque-headed bebe with jointed composition body, mark 7 stamped in blue on the body Bebe Jumeau Depose, 15in. high. £1,045

French bisque child doll by Emile Jumeau, circa 1900, 17½in. high. £2,000

French bisque child doll by Emile Jumeau, circa 1875, 14½in. high £1,690

French bisque child doll by Emile Jumeau, circa 1895, 13in. high. £1,500

A Jumeau bisque doll with real auburn hair wig, French, circa 1880, 20½in. high. £1,320

Bisque headed bebe, mark 1907, with sticker printed Bebe Jumeau, 24in. high. £720

LS
EAU

eau bisque doll, French,
1880, 15in. high. £1,320

A French Jumeau bisque
doll, circa 1880, 30in.
high, together with twenty
pieces of clothing.   £3,300

A bisque-headed bebe,
stamped Tete Jumeau
and body Bebe 'Le Pari-
sien' Medaille d'Or Paris,
23in. high.   £900

ench bisque child
l, stamped Jumeau
daille d'Or Paris,
ca 1890, 13in. high.
£1,500

A bisque headed bebe with
fixed blue yeux fibres and
pierced ears, 15in. high,
impressed 6 body stamped
Jumeau Medaille d'or Paris.
£1,155

Jumeau phonograph bisque
doll in original dress and
straw bonnet, circa 1895,
24in. high.   £3,000

ench bisque child doll
Emile Jumeau, France,
ca 1880, 15in. high.
£2,500

French bisque child doll
by Emile Jumeau, circa
1890, 10in. high. £1,500

Bisque child doll by Emile
Jumeau, France, circa
1880, 17½in. high. £3,000

DOLLS
KAMMER & REINHARDT

German bisque charac-
ter doll by Kammer &
Reinhardt, circa 1915
27in. high.   £2,500

German bisque character baby
by Kammer & Reinhardt,
circa 1915, 12in. high.   £325

German bisque charac-
ter doll by Kammer &
Reinhardt, circa 1915
28in. high.   £4,500

German bisque character
doll, by Kammer & Rein-
hardt, circa 1915, 8½in.
high.   £1,500

A bisque headed character
doll with closed mouth, blue
painted eyes, blonde wig and
jointed composition body,
18in. high, marked K*R 114.46.
                £2,420

German bisque child doll
with brown head and body
by Kammer & Reinhardt,
circa 1915, 22in. high.
                £1,000

A Kammer & Reinhardt
bisque-headed doll with
composition body, 46cm.
high.   £3,000

Bisque character doll by
Kammer & Reinhardt,
circa 1915, in sailor's
costume, 18in. high.
                £800

German bisque walking
child doll, by Kammer &
Reinhardt, circa 1910,
25in. high.   £451

Kathe Kruse cloth
oll, German, circa 1928,
7in. high.   £500

German composition
character doll by Kathe
Kruse, circa 1920, 36in.
high.   £2,500

Kathe Kruse boy doll,
Germany, in original
clothes, circa 1920,
17.3/8in. high. £1,500

An early Kathe Kruse
cloth doll with swivel
joints at hips, German,
circa 1911, 17in. high.
          £935

A painted cloth doll with
brown painted hair, the
stuffed body jointed at hip
and shoulder, by Kathe
Kruse, 17in. high.   £360

Kathe Kruse girl
doll with real hair
wig, 20in. high.£300

A cloth character doll, the
head in five sections, 16in.
high, by Kathe Kruse, and
The Katy Kruse dolly book,
published 1927.   £1,045

Kathe Kruse wistful
doll signed on foot
in purple, 18in. high.
          £400

Early 20th century German
character doll by Kathe Kruse,
17in. high.   £300

DOLLS
KESTNER

German all bisque minia-
ture doll, probably by
Kestner, made for Strobel
& Wilken, circa 1900, 8in.
high.   £138

German bisque character
baby doll by Kestner,
circa 1915, 15in. high.
                          £525

German all bisque minia-
ture doll with blue glass
eyes, by Kestner, circa
1900, 5in. high.   £200

German all bisque
miniature doll, pro-
bably by Kestner,
circa 1890, 8in.
high.   £400

A fine German character doll
by Kestner, with original
clothes, 13in. high, circa 1915.
                          £1,500

German bisque headed
character doll with
'googly' eyes, by J. D.
Kestner, circa 1910, 16in.
high.   £2,870

German all bisque minia-
ture doll, probably by
Kestner, 8in. high.
                          £300

Bisque character doll by J. D.
Kestner, Germany, circa 1915,
15in. high.   £450

German all bisque minia-
ture doll, 7in. high, by
Kestner, circa 1910. £250

German bisque character doll by Kestner, circa 1900, with olive tinted skin, 13in. high. £3,500

A bisque headed character baby doll, 9in. high, marked 142 2/0 by Kestner. £200

German all bisque miniature doll by Kestner, circa 1900, 9½in. high. £300

Bisque adult lady doll by Kestner, circa 1900, in excellent condition, 10in. high. £700

A pair of all bisque doll's house dolls with blue painted eyes, 5in. high, marked 1503 and 1603 on the legs, by Kestner, circa 1910. £143

German bisque character doll by Kestner, circa 1910, with papier-mache body, 8in. high. £550

ll bisque character doll by J. D. estner, circa 1915, 'Our Baby', 0in. high. £350

German bisque miniature doll by J. D. Kestner, circa 1900, in crocheted dress, 8in. high. £450

German bisque character doll by J. D. Kestner, circa 1910, 14in. high. £920

DOLLS
KLEY & HAHN

German bisque character doll with composition bent limb baby body, by Kley & Hahn, circa 1915, 13in. high. £380

German bisque character doll, by Kley & Hahn, circa 1915, 28in. high. £629

German bisque character baby doll, by Kley & Hahn, circa 1915, 17in. high. £570

LEHMANN

German Lehmann mechanical sailor, 7½in. high, circa 1912-14. £275

Early 20th century Lehmann waltzing doll, head with EPL trademark, 9in. high. £625

Lehmann walking sailor, German, circa 1905, 7½in. long, one hand missing. £175

LENCI

Lenci girl, dressed in cerise felt dress, hat and shoes, 1930's, 16in. high. £55

A painted felt doll modelled as a young girl, marked on the feet Lenci, 25in. high. £170

Italian Lenci cloth character doll, by Madame di Scavini, 13in. high. £138

LLS
CI

lian all cloth doll with
t face, by Lenci, circa
25, 17in. high.   £450

Italian all cloth charac-
ter doll with felt
swivel head, by Lenci,
circa 1925, 19in. high.
£2,000

Italian cloth character
Lenci doll, by Madame di
Scavini, circa 1930, 19in.
high.   £170

painted head doll with blue
es, the felt body in original,
thes, 16in. high, marked
nci, circa 1930.   £121

Italian Lenci cloth character doll, by Madame di
Scavini, circa 1925, 17in.
high.   £315

Italian cloth charac-
ter doll by Lenci,
1927, 22in. high.
£2,500

alian cloth character doll,
enci, by Madame di Scavini,
irca 1925, 21in. high. £280

Italian cloth doll by
Madame Lenci, circa
1930, 24in. high, in
original cardboard box.
£700

Lenci doll in provincial costume, circa 1930, 19in. high.
£230

DOLLS
MADAME ALEXANDER

An Israeli doll by Madame Alexander, 1964-73, 8in. high. £100

American plastic character doll by Madame Alexander, circa 1958, 8in. high. £1,000

A Japanese doll with 'Maggie' face, by Madame Alexander, 1964-73, 8in. high. £200

Vinyl character doll by the Alexander Doll Co., circa 1965, 13in. high. £500

American plastic character doll by Madame Alexander, circa 1961, 14in. high. £250

American plastic character doll, 'Prince Charming', by Madame Alexander, circa 1950, 18in. high. £400

American plastic character doll by Madame Alexander, 1975, 22in. high. £255

American plastic fashion doll, circa 1953, by Madame Alexander, 18in. high. £500

American plastic character doll by Madame Alexander, New York, circa 1966-68, 8in. high. £400

Set of four articulated paper dolls, circa
90, each 9in. high.   £75

Set of lithographed paper dolls on heavy
cardboard, depicting Hansel and Gretel,
printed in Germany, circa 1890, 7½in. high.
£25

Group of various paperdolls, including Miss Ida Rehan, 14in. high, by
Raphael Tuck & Sons, 1894.   £355

We're All In It, 'Mummy Puts On Uniform'.
£7.50

Daily Express Doll Dressing Press-Out Book
'Sweden'.   £4

DOLLS
PAPIER-MACHE

An early papier-mache headed doll with painted features, circa 1840, 11in. high. £220

A papier-mache headed autoperipatetikos with brown painted eyes, 10in. high. £350

A papier-mache shoulder headed doll, Sonneburg, circa 1840, 25in. high. £550

A Biedermeier shoulder-papier-mache doll with painted face, circa 1825, 10½in. high. £330

A 19th century papier-mache doll, circa 1850, 7½in. high. £200

19th century miniature papier-mache doll with kid body, circa 1850, 7½in. high. £250

19th century miniature papier-mache doll with kid body, circa 1850, 7½in. high. £250

A papier-mache mask faced doll with turquoise blue eyes, the cloth and wood body in original Central European costume, 15½ in. high, circa 1860. £198

An early shoulder-papier-mache doll in original clothes, French, circa 1840, 11½in. high. £385

DOLLS
PARISIENNE

white bisque shoulder-headed Parisienne doll, French, 13in. high. £450

A bisque swivel headed Parisienne, 17½in. high without stand, the head marked 3. £3,600

A bisque shoulder-headed Parisienne doll, circa 1870, 15½in. high. £400

PORTRAIT

English cloth portrait doll of Edward VIII, circa 1930, 15in. high. £350

A set of composition dolls representing the Dionne quintuplets with doctor and nurse, 7½in. high, the adults 13in. high, by Madame Alexander. £418

An American 'Shirley Temple' personality doll, 21in. high, circa 1935. £475

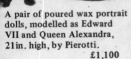

A pair of poured wax portrait dolls, modelled as Edward VII and Queen Alexandra, 21in. high, by Pierotti. £1,100

A composition portrait doll modelled as Shirley Temple, 13½in. high, marked S.T. 5/0 CB Germany. £242

Three Martha Thompson bisque portrait models of The Queen, Prince Charles and Princess Anne. £400

DOLLS
SFBJ

A bisque-headed character
doll, marked SFBJ236
Paris 6 and embossed 21,
14in. high.   £550

French bisque child doll by
SFBJ, Paris, circa 1915,
30in. high.   £1,700

French bisque character
doll by SFBJ, Paris, circa
1915, 19in. high.   £690

A bisque headed doll with glass
eyes, open mouth and composition body, marked S.F.B.J. 60
Paris, 18in. high.   £110

A bisque headed child doll,
marked SFBJ Paris 14, 32in.
high, original box marked
Bebe Francais.   £800

An SFBJ bisque characte
boy doll, impressed 237 $
with jointed composition
body in navy sailor suit,
French, circa 1910, 23in.
high.   £1,430

A bisque-headed charac-
ter baby doll, marked
SFBJ 251 Paris 11, 22½in.
high.   £800

A bisque headed doll, impressed
SFBJ 236 Paris 12, with composition toddler body, circa
1910, 24in. high.   £600

Early 20th century bisque
head character boy doll,
impressed SFBJ 238 Paris
4, France, 17¾in. high.
£2,750

Early 20th century bisque-
head character boy doll,
SFBJ France, 18in. high.
£1,500

A bisque headed character
baby doll, 27in. high, marked
SFBJ252 Paris 12. £1,540

S.F.B.J. bisque headed
doll in lace-trimmed
dress, 45cm. high.£225

A bisque-headed doll with
composition body, 17in.
high, impressed SFBJ60
Paris O. £200

A rare bisque-headed
googly-eyed character
doll, marked SFBJ 245
Paris 4, 13½in. high.
£3,000

French bisque character
doll, SFBJ, circa 1915,
12in. high. £2,240

CHMIDT BRUNO

Rare late 19th century
Bruno Schmidt bisque
Oriental doll, Germany,
16in. high, in original
dress. £1,500

'Wendy' bisque doll by
Bruno Schmidt of Walters-
hausen, circa 1900.
£2,250

Rare Jumeau 19th century
Bruno Schmidt bisque
Oriental doll, Germany,
16in. high, in original dress.
£2,000

DOLLS
SCHOENAU & HOFFMEISTER

Schoenau and
Hoffmeister doll
with blue eyes,
26in. tall, circa
1909.   £150

A Schoenau & Hoffmeis-
ter 'Princess Elizabeth'
bisque doll, circa 1938,
16in. high.   £1,000

A Schoenau & Hoffmeister
shoulder-bisque Marotte
doll, German, circa 1900,
15in. high.   £350

SCHOENHUT

American carved wooden
character doll with brown
intaglio eyes, by Schoen-
hut of Philadelphia, circa
1911, 15in. high.   £312

Wooden character doll by
Schoenhut, Philadelphia,
12in. high, circa 1915.
    £230

American wooden charact-
doll, by Schoenhut of Phil-
delphia, circa 1911, 16in.
high.   £42

American wooden charac-
ter doll with intaglio
brown eyes, by Schoen-
hut of Philadelphia, circa
1911, 15in. high.   £243

American carved wooden doll and
animal, 'Milkmaid and Cow', by
Schoenhut of Philadelphia, each
8in.   £416

American wooden charac-
ter doll by Albert Schoenhut, circa 1915, 18in. hig
    £300

OLLS
IMON & HALBIG

Simon & Halbig walking/
talking doll with jointed
body, 20in. high. £450

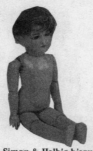

A Simon & Halbig bisque
headed doll with composition
ball jointed body, 24in. high.
£340

Bisque child doll by
Simon & Halbig,
Germany, circa 1900,
41in. high.   £450

Simon & Halbig bisque
headed doll, Germany,
circa 1880, 12½in. high.
£750

Early 20th century 'Googly'
doll by Simon & Halbig.
£2,500

Late 19th century Simon &
Halbig bisque Oriental doll,
12in. high.   £1,250

Bisque lady doll by
Simon & Halbig, circa
1880, 10½in. high,
with unusual swivel
neck.   £700

Japanese doll by
Simon and Halbig.
£1,250

A bisque headed child doll
with fixed brown eyes and
blonde wig, 10in. high,
marked 1079 DEP S&H.
£187

DOLLS
SIMON & HALBIG

A bisque headed child doll,
8½in. high, marked 1078
S&H.   £264

German bisque character
doll by Simon & Halbig,
21in. high.   £800

A German bisque walking
doll by Simon & Halbig,
circa 1890, 16½in. high.
                  £1,500

A Simon & Halbig bisque
doll impressed 1079, with
jointed wood and compo-
sition body, German, circa
1890, 28in., together with
a pair of kid doll's gloves.
                  £550

A clockwork toy of a bisque
headed doll pulling a two-
wheeled cart, marked 1079
Halbig S & H 7½, by Toullet
Decamps.   £550

A bisque-headed character
child doll, 23in. high,
marked K*R Simon and
Halbig 117n58, and a boy
doll, 22in. high.   £935

Simon & Halbig bisque
child doll with clockwork
mechanism, circa 1890,
22in. high.   £670

A Simon & Halbig bisque
headed Jutta character doll,
impressed 'Jutta 1914 12',
circa 1920, 21in. high. £440

German bisque child
doll by Simon &
Halbig, circa 1920,
14in. high.   £600

DOLLS
SIMON & HALBIG

Simon & Halbig version of the Gibson Girl, circa 1900, 15in. high. £675

A Simon & Halbig bisque 'walking' doll, German, circa 1890, 13in. high. £450

A bisque-headed charac- ter toddler doll, marked Simon & Halbig, 26in. high. £600

A bisque-headed child doll, 22in. high, marked Handwerck 109-11 Halbig on the shoes, NAPAUD 32 rue du 4 Septembre. £825

Very rare late 19th century black bisque doll, impressed 7 1302 Dep S & H, 19½in. high. £6,000

A bisque-headed character doll, marked 1488 Simon & Halbig 4, 12½in. high. £1,650

A Simon & Halbig bisque lady doll, with open mouth and upper teeth, German, circa 1910, 27in. high. £1,320

Simon & Halbig bisque character doll, wooden ball-jointed body with adult modelling, circa 1900, 27in. high. £10,450

A Simon & Halbig bisque doll, impressed 1079, in original crocheted underclothes, Ger- man, circa 1890, 13in. high. £330

DOLLS
SIMON & HALBIG/KAMMER & REINHARDT

Kammer & Reinhardt/ Simon & Halbig bisque doll with jointed body, 26in. high. £500

A bisque-headed character child doll, 23in. high, marked K*R Simon and Halbig 117n58, and a boy doll, 22in. high. £935

Kammer & Reinhardt/Simon & Halbig 'My Darling' doll with jointed body, 22in. high £2,000

Bisque character headed baby doll marked K*R,S. & H., 114/A, 18in. high. £1,750

Simon & Halbig/Kammer & Reinhardt bisque-headed doll, 1914-27, 26in. high. £470

A Kammer & Reinhardt/ Simon & Halbig bisque character doll, impressed 121 42, German, circa 1910, 17in. high. £460

A Kammer & Reinhardt/ Simon & Halbig bisque character doll impressed 126 24, German, circa 1910, 11in. high. £264

One of two bisque headed doll's house dolls with blue sleeping eyes, one with brown wig, 5½in. high, one marked Halbig K*R 13. £286

A bisque headed character child doll with blue sleeping eyes, marked K*R SH115/A 42, 16½in. high. £2,300

116

DOLLS
STEINER

French walking doll by Jules N. Steiner, circa 1880, 15in. high. **£600**

Steiner Patent walking bisque doll in blue dress with lace overdress, 15in. high circa 1880. **£750**

French Jules Steiner bourgoin bisque doll, circa 1880, 18½in. high. **£2,750**

Good Steiner clockwork walking/talking doll with papier-mache and kid body, 18in. high. **£700**

A bisque headed bebe with jointed composition and wood body, by Steiner, 12in. high. **£1,100**

French bisque automaton by Jules Nicholas Steiner, circa 1890, 20in. high. **£955**

A Steiner Motschmann-type bisque doll, France, circa 1860, with fixed glass eyes, 12¾in. high. **£1,307**

Steiner Patent walking bisque doll in original dress and jacket, circa 1860, 15¼in. high. **£1,500**

A bisque-headed bebe with fixed blue eyes, marked J. Steiner Bte SGDG Paris Fre A9, 10in. high. **£675**

DOLLS
STEINER

French bisque child doll,
beautifully dressed, by
Jules Steiner, circa 1890,
19½in. high.   £1,750

A bisque headed bebe, marked
J. Steiner Paris, SreA.3, 11in.
high.   £800

Steiner talking bisque doll
in original lace dress, circa
1880, 17½in. high.   £750

A bisque-headed bebe, marked
SteA.2 and written in red
Steiner A.S.G.D.G. Paris
Bourgoin jeun, and a wig,
18in. high.   £1,650

A bisque headed bebe with
composition jointed body,
marked FTE C 3/0 by
Steiner, 10in. high. £1,200

Steiner bisque head girl doll
with five-piece composition
body, Paris, circa 1890, 9in.
high.   £454

French bisque child doll,
by Jules N. Steiner, circa
1885, 14in. high. £1,250

A bisque headed clockwork
Bebe Premier Pas with kid
upper legs and blonde wig,
17½in. high, by Jules Nicholas
Steiner, circa 1890.   £1,100

Rare Jules Steiner Bour-
goin bisque portrait doll
in original suit, circa 1880,
29in. high.   £5,000

American cloth charac-
ter doll by Izannah
Walker, circa 1870,
18in. high.   £7,875

An Izannah Walker doll with
brushed hair and painted
boots, circa 1873, 17in.
high.   £4,365

American cloth character
doll, produced by Izannah
Walker of Rhode Island,
circa 1860, 26in. high.
£965

AX

A poured shoulder-wax
doll with fixed blue glass
eyes, English, circa 1880,
18½in. high.   £352

Charlotte Norris, a wax-over-
composition headed doll with
smiling mouth, the stuffed body
with pink kid arms, 23in. high,
1840-45.   £308

A wax over composition
shoulder headed doll with
short, blonde, curly wool
wig, 1810-15, 14in. high.
£240

A poured-wax child doll with
ace edged underclothes,
irca 1851, 13in. high. £320

A poured shoulder-wax
doll, English, circa 1860,
20in. high.   £550

A poured-wax child doll
with fixed pale blue eyes,
20in. high, in box. £380

DOLLS
WAX

A poured-wax child doll
with fixed blue eyes,
21in. high.   £500

A wax over composition
headed pedlar doll, 12in.
wide, under glass dome.
£650

A wax over composition
bonnet headed doll with
wooden limbs, 12½in.
high.   £250

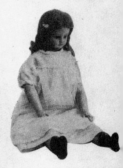

19th century wax over papier-
mache doll, circa 1860, 20in.
high.   £220

A Pierotti poured shoul-
der-wax doll, English,
1870, 19½in. high.
£420

A waxed shoulder composi-
tion doll with painted closed
mouth and fixed blue eyes,
30in. high.   £310

A shoulder-waxed-compo-
sition doll, German, circa
1880, 16in. high, right
arm loose.   £121

A waxed shoulder-compo-
sition doll, circa 1880,
21½in. high, slight crack-
ing to face.   £220

Early wax head swaddling
baby, circa 1840, 18in.
high.   .£420

LS

poured shoulder-wax
ale doll, the stuffed
ody with wax limbs,
rca 1860, 18in. high.
£300

A poured shoulder-wax
doll, English, circa 1860,
23in. high.   £330

Late 1820's wax shoulder-
headed doll with painted
brown hair, 12in. high.
(damaged).   £200

wax over composition
eaded doll with smiling
ainted face, circa 1878,
n. high.   £75

A wax composition doll,
with sleeping blue eyes,
fair wig and stuffed cloth
body, 14in. long.   £280

A wax over composition
shoulder headed doll,
the blue eyes wired from
the waist.   £300

wax-headed figure of a
ashionable woman, with
abel reading Meurillon et
ie, Paris, 11½in. high.
£150

A poured-wax child doll with
blue wired sleeping eyes, the
stuffed body with bisque
limbs in original nightgown,
21in. high.   £320

A shoulder-waxed-compo-
sition doll with blonde
mohair plaited wig, German,
circa 1880, 18in. high.
£308

**DOLLS
WOOD**

An early English wooden
doll, circa 1770, 16½in.
high.   £3,500

A George III wooden
doll with painted face,
circa 1780, 20in. high.
                £3,250

A George I wooden doll,
the gesso-covered head with
finely painted blushed cheeks
English, circa 1725, 16in. high
                £12,10

American carved wooden
swivel headed doll by Joel
Ellis, circa 1878, 13in.
high.   £694

Two wooden rod puppets
with painted faces. £100

Late 18th century East
European wooden doll
with pinned ball joints,
height to knee 21¼in.
                £2,090

A turned and painted
wooden doll with inset
enamel eyes, circa 1810,
14in. high, in a wooden
glazed case.   £1,500

A William and Mary wooden
doll with a wisp of real auburn hair and nailed-on stitched
linen wig, English, circa 1690,
16¾in. high.   £17,600

A painted wooden child doll
the jointed wooden body (one
foot missing) 17in. high, probably by Schilling.   £198

122

ɔinted wooden doll with
nted features and real
nd hair wig, circa 1845.
£240

An early 19th century crudely
carved wood doll with blue enamel
and nail eyes and painted limbs,
15½in. high.   £150

An English mid 19th cen-
tury vendor doll of wood
and cloth, under glass dome
with turned walnut base,
16in. high.   £2,112

rench wooden manne-
uin doll with articula-
ed body, 20th century,
1in. high.   £300

An early 19th century group
of painted wooden headed
dolls, 'There was an old
woman who lived in a shoe',
5in. long.   £120

Mid 18th century wooden
doll in contemporary
costume.   £3,500

George II wooden doll
h blonde real hair nailed-
wig, English, circa 1750,
n. high.   £11,000

'Lord and Lady Clapham',
William and Mary wooden
dolls.   £16,000

Carved wooden shoulder-
head doll with original odd-
shaped straw stuffed muslin
body, probably Austrian,
circa 1910.   £355

DOLL'S HOUSES

A lithographic paper on wood doll's house with decorative front porch and balcony, 12½in., German, circa 1915. £350

Victorian painted doll's house with portico doorway flanked by columns, English, circa 1890, 32½in. high by 37½in. wide £1,

A late Victorian wooden doll's house in the shape of a two-storey villa, with pitched slate roof, front divided and hinged, 71 x 33cm. £750

Doll's house copied from original family house with Gothic shaped door, gabled roof and two chimneys, English, circa 1910, 33in. high by 39½in. wide. £1,500

A lithographic paper on wood doll's house, with steps leading to front door, 13in. high, American, circa 1910. £300

Early 20th century American wooden gabled roof doll's house with glass windows, 24¾in. high. £2

Victorian wooden doll's house, cottage
style, with working door with brass
knob at front, circa 1890.   £1,080

A custom crafted Colonial-style doll's house,
circa 1980, with ten rooms of furniture,
rugs, textiles and accessories, 28in. high,
53¾in. long.   £1,200

An early 20th century doll's house, paper
overed to simulate brickwork, 88cm. high.
                                          £290

An early 20th century two-storeyed doll's
house, facade 20 x 18in., depth 12in.   £280

A Jacobean style wood and composition
doll's house of four bays and two storeys,
27in. wide.   £385

American diorama of an early 19th century
hallway, circa 1950, fitted with dolls and
furniture, 19½in. wide.   £150

DOLL'S HOUSES

An English Gothic-styled Victorian doll's house with steeply gabled roof, circa 1870. £440

English late 19th century interior of an open room in Georgian style, 23in. wide. £495

A doll's house, the gabled roo with pocket watch movement mounted within the pediment 34in. wide. £242

19th century wooden Mansard roof doll's house with painted brick front, 23¾in. high. £225

A model doll's house of Harethorpe Hall, a two-storye mansion, with painted brick front, 23 x 47 x 13in. deep. £800

Belgian doll's house, modelled as a detached town villa with three bays, 1870's. £2,400

A 19th century wooden kitchen, maker unknown, several pieces marked Germany, 26 x 15 x 15in. £1,335

Late 19th century yellow Victorian doll's house and furniture, 26¾in. wide. £230

126

wooden doll's house
nted to simulate stone-
rk of two bays and
storeys, circa 1850,
n. approx.　　　£300

English late 19th century painted
wooden doll's house of Victorian
design, 42in. wide.　　　£660

A large Victorian doll's house
with two hinged front sections, mounted on wheels,
circa 1890, 40in. wide.£660

Large doll's house in the form of a two-storey
suburban house with arched roof, English,
circa 1930, 45in. high by 73in. long.　　　£850

A wooden doll's house painted to simulate
stonework of five bays and three storeys,
46in. wide.　　　£3,800

printed paper on wood doll's
ouse, by Lines Bros., 43in.
ide.　　　£935

A painted wooden doll's box-
type town house of three bays
and three storeys, 25in. high.
£330

American wooden doll's house
by the Bliss Toy Co., Rhode
Island, circa 1900, 18 x 12 x
9in.　　　£383

FIRE ENGINES

Keystone sheet metal fire truck, circa 1930, 28in. long.   £300

Early 20th century child's metal toy fire truck painted red.   £20(

A 2in. scale model of a horse-drawn 1875 Shand Mason fire engine, 21in. long overall.   £2,860

A Schuco 6080 Elektro-Construction t plate fire engine, in original box, circa 1955.   £2

A 1½in. scale model of a spirit-fired Shand-Mason horsedrawn fire engine of 1894.
£800

'Fire Brigade', a printed and painted tinpla fire engine, 15½in. long, by Distler, circa 1936.   £28(

A Distler tinplate and clockwork fire engine, 37.5cm. long overall.   £350

A Bing hand-enamelled model of an early fire engine, circa 1902, 10½in. long.   £75(

AMES

1930's leather 'Disappearing Banknote' pocket novelty. £1

Early 20th century tartan-ware whist marker. £5

American 'General Grant's marble game', circa 1870, diam. of marbles 1.1/8in. £365

Tut-Tut or A Run In A Motor Card, A New and Exciting Game, with forty-eight cards depicting an Edwardian open tourer, contained in original box. £70

'A Figuren Alphabetspeil', a set of twenty fine printed paper on wood alphabet blocks German, circa 1910. £300

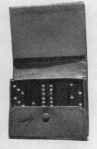

Leatherette wallet with integral domino set. £3

Victorian pictorial play block, 4in. square. £3

Victorian box of wooden building bricks, 9in. square. £8

GAMES

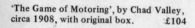

'The Game of Motoring', by Chad Valley, circa 1908, with original box. £104

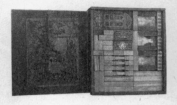

Victorian wooden building game in a fine pictorial box. £

'Steeplechase & Race Game'. £12

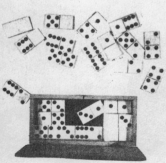

Victorian set of bone dominoes in an oak box. £48

'The Portland Chess & Draughts Board', Robinson & Sons. £2

GAMES

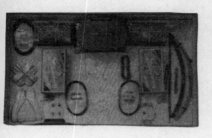

A Schuco-Varianto 3010 Motorway, in original box, US Zone W. Germany, circa 1955. £121

'Find the Car', by C. W. Faulkner, 1920. £2.50

'Improved Greek Architecture' wooden puzzle. £25

'James Bond, Secret Service Game', Spear's.£10

Late 19th century parquetry folding cribbage board. £5

'The Popular Game of Halma', Squadron Edition. £4

'Wireless Whist, Score Cards', The Dainty Series, 1920's. £2.50

HORSE-DRAWN VEHICLES

A model of a Dorset Wagon, complete with hay racks, carved light draught horse, dog, carter and a small pack mule, carved by George Gill of Branscombe. £900

A Lehmann 'Bulky Mule' tinplate toy, No. 425, German, circa 1920, 7in. wide. £187

Cast-iron circus van, red enclosed wagon, red driver and two black horses, circa 1920's. £100

A zebra cart toy, probably French, circa 1900, 10½in. long. £220

Dent cast iron three horse hook and ladder, early 1900's, 29in. long. £300

A German tinplate horse-drawn open carriage finished in cream and green, the felt covered tinplate horse supported on a flywheel setting the horse in motion. £1,000

Late 19th century Wilkins cast iron trolley, 'Broadway Car Line 712', 12in. long. £1,212

A late 19th century wooden model Hay-wain, 26in. long overall. £104

HORSE-DRAWN VEHICLES

Cast-iron Police Patrol wagon, black trotting horse pulls open yellow wagon, with driver and three policemen, 11in. long, circa 1910. £100

Late 19th century painted 'Dandy Dan' riding horse toy, America, 3ft.9in. long.£400

Bulky Mule, The Stubborn Donkey', EPL 25, by Lehmann, circa 1920, 7½in. long. £110

Britain's Farm, horse-drawn milk float with milkman and two churns, No. 131F, in original box. (Milkman has broken neck.) £48

Late 19th century painted tin horsedrawn coach, overall length 29in. £1,665

An F. Martin tinplate Hansom Cab, French, circa 1905, 9in. long. £242

A model of a horse-drawn cart by Benefink & Co. £390

A Britains' farmer's gig, No. F28 with horse, together with Fordson tractor, unboxed.£30

'The Romans at Caerleon', one of the series of 43
puzzles made by Chad Valley for the G.W.R. Co.
during the 1920's and 1930's. Box of slip-case
type from the 1930's, 14 x 14in.   £19

'The Eton Coach', popular or fashionable artists' works were often the
subjects of jigsaw puzzles between the wars. This one, of a Cecil Aldin
painting, has been cut in the style of the Huvanco firm, 6 x 19in. £14

'The Horse', one of a series of 'Graphic illustrations of animals showing
their utility to man', by Roake & Varty, circa 1840, 12 x 15in.   £70

'Primrose and Violet', with traditional shapes, an early Victory (Hayter &
Co.), with interesting box design showing common pictorial theme of
the period, 1920's, 11 x 13in.   £17

135

JIGSAW PUZZLES

'The Victory', one of The Delta Fine Cut
'National' Series of puzzles from the 1930's.
The box lid bears a traditional design that
has a family resemblance to the Victory box,
13 x 18in.   £19

'The Milkmaid', 1930's 'Chandos' puzzle by Frederick Warne, it has a
distinctive and easily-recognisable style of cut which can make it
awkward to assemble, 7 x 9in.   £10

136

'First Whiff', a Lawson Wood cartoon made into a puzzle, probably by an amateur, 1930's. Humour was always a popular subject for amateurs (who often cut to professional standards, and usually with an interpretive flair) and Lawson Wood has become highly collectible now, 10 x 8in.   £14

Double sided puzzles became very popular during the inter-war jigsaw 'craze' years; they were mass produced on a large scale, since they offered 'two for the price of one'. This one has typically sentimental subject for each side, 7 x 10in.   £7

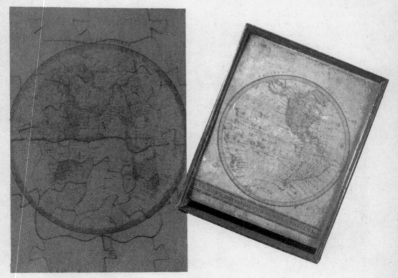

A rare Barfoot puzzle, a double sided map dissection, showing the Eastern and Western hemispheres (normally Barfoot had a non-map picture — eg historical or mathematical tables — on the reverse side of a map), 12 x 8in., circa 1855.   £220

JIGSAW PUZZLES

'A Labour of Love', 'Society Dissected Picture Puzzle — The Latest Craze' made for Hamley Bros. to sell in their store in London during the 1920's. The box label is typical of those made also for other stores, who had their names printed in the space provided, 8 x 6in.
£8

'Journey into Egypt', probably amateur cut, all pushfit pieces, typical of its type and style for the period, 1920's, 9 x 7in.
£9

'Captain Cuttle', one of a series of twelve Dickens characters made into puzzles and issued by A. V. N. Jones in the 1930's, 10 x 8in.
£19

138

DOLLS & TOYS

'Good Companions', 1930's example of a Douglas Jigsaw Library Puzzle, with its unusual and unrepetitive shapes that make it more challenging to assemble, 14 x 18in. £15

'A Welcome Intrusion', a 1930's Chad Valley puzzle with its characteristic patented—'book-box' design of container with guide picture, 10 x 14in. £12

JIGSAW PUZZLES

Snow White, Walt Disney, 1938. £7.50

Jigsaw Puzzle, John Wallis's chronological Tables of English History for the Instruction of Youth, 1788, one piece missing.   £120

'Coronation 1953', a characteristic commemorative puzzle of the 1950's by Victory, the box is large enough to take the fully assembled puzzle, 8 x 10in.   £18

Dissected Map of Scotland, by Peacock, 19th century. £35

Anne Hathaways Cottage, Great Western Railway Jigsaw 1930.   £15

'Sporting Days', a 1920's Raphael Tuck 'Oilette' picture puzzle by H. Drummond, 6 x 9in.   £17

JIGSAW PUZZLES

Coronation Jigsaw Puzzle, 1953. £2

BBC TV 'Dr Who and the Daleks', 1973. £6

The Duke of Edinburgh, Victory Jigsaw. £2

Famous Footballers, No. 1, Tommy Lawton. £2

Giselle, Victory Plywood Jigsaw, 1950's. £2

The Piglets, Beatles Take-Off, Waddington's, 1964. £3

LEAD FIGURES

Britains set of South African Mounted
Infantry in its original box.   £500

Britains set No 1470, The Coronation
State Coach, including eight Windsor grays,
four outriders, H.M. Queen Elizabeth II and
Prince Philip, in gold painted state coach, in
original box.   £200

Heyde 30mm. hand-painted Indian elephant,
with howdah, containing Maharajah and
bower, an Indian lancer, 5 palm trees, six
54mm. scale figures and six other figures.
                                                 £150

A collection of Britains and other makers
World War I soldiers and some trees, circa
1920.   £50

Britain's Set No. 2, The Royal Horse Guards,
one officer and four troopers, at the trot,
bearing swords (one sword missing), box
torn but with label intact.   £75

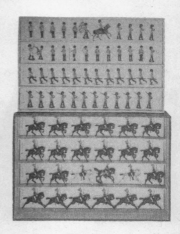

Large display box Set 93, containing Coldstream Guards with mounted officer, four
pioneers, thirteen-piece band, two officers,
twelve marching, twelve running, two
trumpeters, six troopers and fifteen normal
troopers, 1938, Britain's.   £7,000

Royal Horse Artillery at the halt, Service
Dress with peak caps, khaki uniform,
Set 318, in original box, Britain's. £6,500

LEAD FIGURES

Britains set No. 37, Band of the Coldstream Guards. £200

Britains set No. 315, 10th Royal Hussars, Prince of Wales' Own, at the halt with swords and bugler, in original box. £250

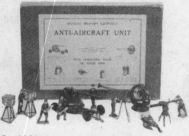

Set 2052, Anti-Aircraft Unit with AA gun, searchlight and instruments and operating crew of eight men, in original box, 1959 Britain's. £650

A collection of 38 French soldiers and Zouaves, including ski troops and one mule, made in France, circa 1940. £70

A mixed collection of 15 lead models, including soldiers, cowboys and red indians, Spanish warship blowing up, two men-of-war, etc., circa early 1920's. £22

Elastolin 100mm. scale hand-painted composition soldiers, Coldstream Guards, marching at slope arms in full equipment. £550

Royal Horse Artillery at the gallop in steel helmets, Set 1339, in original box, 1940 Britain's £7,000

Three officers mounted on galloping chargers and two armed Africans riding on a camel, circa early 1920's. £20

LEAD FIGURES

Britains set No. 315, 10th Royal Hussars, Prince of Wales' Own, at the halt with swords, and bugler, in original box. £300

Britains Attendants to the State Coach, including walking outriders, footmen of the Royal Household and Yeomen, in original box. £150

Britains Royal Air Force, set 2011, twenty-two pieces. £180

Two Whistock boxes of Britains King's Royal Rifle Corps, No. 98, each box containing eight figures, circa 1905. £200

Britains extremely rare display set 131, the largest set ever made by Britains, consisting of 281 figures including cavalrymen, infantrymen, bandsmen, sailors and Camel Corps soldiers, circa 1905. £10,000

Eight British Boer War soldiers wearing tropical helmets, in their original box. £65

A Britains set No. 434, R.A.F. Monoplane, with two pilots and four R.A.F. personnel, in original box. £1,000

LEAD FIGURES

Britains set No. 1634, The Governor-General's Foot Guards, marching at the slope arms, with officer, in original box. (Christie's) £100

Britains early set No. 211, 18in. Howitzer No. 2, with ten horse team, in review order with No. 2 Howitzer and limber, in original box. £1,000

A Britains boxed set of The Royal Horse Artillery gun team. £6,200

Two Whistock boxes of Britains Bluejackets, No. 78, each box containing eight figures, circa 1905. £200

A Britains R.A.M.C. 4-horse covered ambulance waggon, in original linen cover, with 2 A.S.C. drivers and 2 seated R.A.M.C. orderlies, all full dress, and R.A.M.C. officer, nurse and stretcher. (Wallis & Wallis) £175

Twelve German made solid pewter model Boer soldiers, 45mm. high, circa 1900, in their original red box. £70

Part of an eighteen piece set of Britains model hunt, unboxed. £50

MINIATURE FURNITURE

Miniature Biedermeier nightstand with marble top and tiny oval mirror, 1in. scale.   £77

A George III miniature mahogany chest of drawers, 14¾in. wide.   £90

Contemporary miniature hanging cradel, by Carol Anderson, painted by Natasha, 1981, 1in. scale.   £104

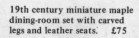

Miniature Chippendale style wing chair and stool with walnut cabriole legs, chair 4½in. high.   £30

19th century miniature maple dining-room set with carved legs and leather seats.   £75

Contemporary wooden child's chair made by Eugene Beshenkovsky and painted by Natasha 1982, 1in. scale.   £2

A burr-yew wood miniature chest inlaid with lines, on bracket feet, 11in. wide.   £2,860

An American late Federal mahogany miniature chest of drawers, 10in. wide.   £733

A 19th century painted miniature ladder-back armchair, American.   £136

INIATURE FURNITURE

Miniature 19th century Biedermeier type dressing table, 5in. long, trimmed n marble-like stripes.
£150

Late 19th century Japanese miniature steel and gold overlay cabinet on stand, 5.7/8in. high.
£1,000

Miniature natural wood finish armoire with three working cupboard doors, 5 x 4in.   £227

Miniature contemporary canopy bed in walnut with quilted cover, 7½in. high.   £105

Set of 19th century miniature maple wood furniture including a writing desk and two chairs, desk 5½in. wide. £100

A 19th century miniature tilt-top tea table, 13in. high.
£166

Charles I miniature oak cupboard with diamond-inlaid panels, circa 1640, 2ft.7in. wide. £2,860

A miniature apprentice made marquetry top table.   £150

19th century miniature maple wood piano with functioning keyboard, 5in. wide.   £30

MINIATURE FURNITURE

An American, 19th century, miniature painted bannister-back armchair, 9½in. high. £326

A 19th century miniature grain painted bowfront chest-of-drawers, American or English, 12in. high. £798

A 19th century, American miniature classical maple fiddleback chair, 10¾in. high, 8¼in. wide. £36

Mid 18th century miniature Chippendale cherrywood chest-of-drawers, 7¾in. high. £1,016

An American, 18th century, miniature Queen Anne maple and pine slant-front desk, with a cherrywood mirror, the desk 11in. high. £2,322

Late 19th century miniature Chippendale walnut slant-front desk, American, 7¼in. high. £1,0

Late 18th century miniature George III mahogany side table, English, 6in. high. £217

Late 18th century miniature Chippendale mahogany chest-on-chest, English, 16¾in. high. £1,233

An American, 19th century miniature Federal mahoga four-post bedstead with canopy, 15½in. high. £21

MINIATURE FURNITURE

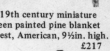

...y 19th century miniature
...eral mahogany oxbow
...st-of-drawers, New England,
...in. high.   £2,903

Early 19th century miniature
Federal mahogany tilt-top
tea table, American, 9in. high.
£653

A 19th century miniature
green painted pine blanket
chest, American, 9½in. high.
£217

...9th century miniature
...eral mahogany picture
...ror, American, 9½in.
...h.   £798

A 17th century miniature oak
coffer of panelled construction,
probably French, 35 x 21 x
23cm.   £700

Late 18th/early 19th
century miniature
Continental painted
tall clock case, 17in.
high   £362

...iniature Chippendale
...ogany desk and bookcase,
...de Island, 1760-80, 16in.
...h.   £1,378

Two 19th century miniature
painted side chairs, American,
9¾in. and 8¼in. high.   £348

A Dutch mahogany and oak
miniature clothes press, 21in.
wide, 33in. high.   £1,980

MINIATURE FURNITURE

A Federal mahogany
miniature chest of
drawers, 1790-1810,
14½in. wide.   £623

19th century tin piano, 3½
x 4in., in excellent condition.
                        £60

Miniature raised panelle
settle by David S. White
                        £27

Part of a set of 20th century miniature wooden furniture
in Colonial Windsor style.   £125

A doll's Jacobean style chair
upholstered in dark red velvet, 21in. high.   £700

A mid Georgian walnut miniature chest, the base with one
long drawer on bracket feet,
13½in. wide.   £1,210

A William and Mary walnut
oyster veneer and cross-
banded chest of small size.
                        £2,000

A miniature Federal sec
tary, America, circa 18
13½in. wide.   £1,8

150

MINIATURE FURNITURE

Biedermeier miniature writing desk with marble writing surface, 3½ x 4½in. £87

Part of a set of 19th century miniature maple wood furniture of a Gothic style settee and a set of shelves. £70

A mid 19th century mahogany miniature tripod table, circa 1840, 9½in. diam. £209

Miniature Napoleonic-style bed and chairs, 4½ x 4in. £160

Group of 19th century miniature furniture of a cupboard and three chairs, cupboard 7½in. high. £65

A Victorian mahogany and marquetry banded miniature chest of five drawers, 14in. wide. £200

An Anglo-Indian miniature ivory bureau cabinet. £7,200

A 19th century miniature, Empire mahogany and painted chest-of-drawers, American, 19½in. wide. £484

151

MINIATURES

Miniature gilt parlour lamp with a white milk glass shade, 1in. scale. **£262**

19th century group of stove accessories each 1½in. high, in excellent condition. **£16**

A metal framed child's mangle with wooden ro **£**

Japanese porcelain child's teaset, each piece illustrates a scene from Little Orphan Annie, circa 1920. **£335**

Miniature wicker fernery with high woven handle, 7in. high. **£20**

A miniature tin dresser, 3½in. wide. **£3**

A miniature cast metal mangle, 5in. high. **£7**

Set of tableware in wooden case with red suede lined interior, 1 x 2in. **£65**

Pearson's miniature diction. including magnifying glass, x ¾in. **£**

Contemporary silver cash
register in 19th century style,
1¼ in. high.   £16

German miniature tin
penny toy with handle
which turns and pro-
duces a music-like sound.
£41

A 19th century miniature
wallpapered bandbox,
American, 4½ in. high. £196

19th century hanging
wall clock, 3½ x 1½ in.,
with brass clock frame.
£45

Miniature Austrian set of porcelain and
silver cutlery of nineteen pieces, in
excellent condition.   £145

Miniature 19th century
banquet lamp with brown
glass shade, 3 in. high.
£60

A miniature violin in original
case with mother-of-pearl
inlay, the case 5 in. long.
£260

A miniature set of die cast
'pots and pans' by Crescent.
£5

A presentation child's set
of French 19th century
Victorian miniature dishes
in case, 17 x 19 in. £250

153

MODEL AIRCRAFT

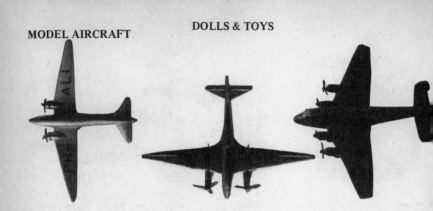

Douglas Air Liner No. 60T, (supposed to be a DC3 by many, but is probably a DC2).   £55

DM Comet Racer No. 60G, 1935-41.   £35

A post-war Giant High Speed Monoplane No. 62Y, R/H Gree.   £25

French Meccano Farman 360, No. 61C, 1935-40.   £60

Japanese Aeromini 747, 1973 -77.   £50

Gladiator Fighter No. 60P, 1937-41.   £40

Kings Aeroplane (Envoy) No. 62K, 1938-41. £45

Air France Caravelle No. 997 — £30 for an English one or £45 for one of French manufacture.

Amiot 370 No. 64AZ, French sold in U.K., 1939 40.   £25

JU89 Heavy Bomber, 67A, 1940-41, German markings. £100

Comet 4 Airliner No. 702, 1954-65. £16

The first Dinky boxed set, No. 60, issued in 1934 to 1940. £300

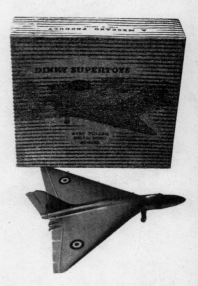

Avro Vulcan No. 992, issued 1955, (not issued in U.K., unknown number released in Canada). £1,200

BEA Viscount No. 708, 1957-65. £25

A pair of Fairey Battles, known as the Mirror Image Pair, 1939-40. £100

MODEL AIRCRAFT

A pre-war Empire Flying Boat No. 60R, 1937. £45

French Meccano Mystere IUA, No. 60A 1957-63. £1?

Mayo Composite Aircraft No. 63, 1939-41. £90

Shetland Flying Boat No. 701, 1947-49. £175

Imperial Airways Liner No. 60A, 1934-40. £75

French Meccano Sikorsky S.58 Helicopter No. 60D, 1957-61. £1?

Frobisher Class Air Liner No. 62R, 1939-41. £45

Air France Viscount No. 706, 1956-57. £3?

156

Tempest II Fighter No. 70B, 1946-55. £8

Bristol Britannia No. 998, 1959-65. £45

JU90 Air Liner No. 62N, 1938-41. £70

Iomica (Japanese) F-14A Tomcat, 1978-80.
£15

Lockheed Constellation No. 60C, produced
by Meccano France, 1957-63.   £100

A pre-war Giant High Speed Monoplane No.
62Y, R/H Gree.   £45

Hawker Hunter No. 736, 1955-63. £7

Japanese Aeromini F-4 Phantom, 1973-77.
£30

MODEL AIRCRAFT

Large monoplane model, made by Charles R.
Witteman, Staten Island, New York, circa
1912, 62in. long, wingspan 78in.   £1,123

A model of a Bleriot-type (Morane) mo
plane, with engine, wingspan 40½in.

A Lehmann Ikarus tinplate aeroplane, No. 653,
German, 10½in. long.   £990

Tipp Co., clockwork lithographed bombe
bi-plane TC-1029, wing span 36.5cm.,
25.5cm. long, key, lacking pilot, three bo
£3

A Marklin monoplane in cream and green,
fitted to a double bogie, plane 20cm.
long.   £200

A Britain's set No. 434, R.A.F. Monopla
with two pilots and four R.A.F. personn
in original box.   £1,200

A 1:24th scale wood and metal model of the
Royal Aircraft Factory SE5a, built by R.
Walden, 1976.   £170

Biplane No. 24, with clockwork mechan
Deutsche Lufthansa markings, wingspan
20¼in. long, by Tipp, circa 1939.

DEL AIRCRAFT

nch tinplate Paris-Tokio bi-plane, clock-
k mechanism driving the wheels, circa
5, 9in. long.   £250

A J.D.N. clockwork tinplate model bi-plane,
made circa 1928.   £450

Iettoy jet airliner, No. 2016/1, in original
with four mechanical sparking replace-
nts, the box 20½in., English, circa 1935.
                                                        £200

'Strato Clipper', a printed and painted tinplate
four-engine airliner with battery mechanism,
by Gama, circa 1956, wingspan 20in.   £104

re-war Japanese R101 airship by GK, the
ninium body with tinplate gondolas and
, 13in. long, together with newspaper
tings, circa 1930.   £450

A flying scale model of the Gloster Gladiator
single seater fighter Serial No. K.8032 with
external details, finished in silver with R.A.F.
markings, wingspan 56in.   £380

nerican Flyer Manufacturing Co., Model
. 560 spring-driven monoplane, 54cm.
g, span 60cm., boxed.   £180

An Exhibition Standard 1:30 scale model of
the prototype Panavia Tornado F-2 Multi
Role Combat Aircraft, wingspan 17½in.
                                                      £2,600

MODEL AIRCRAFT

Post-war Spitfire No. 62A, 1945-49. £10

60u Armstrong Whitworth Whitley No. 62T, Silver 1937-41. £75

Shooting Star No. 70F, 19 62. £

719 Dinky Spitfire, 1969-78. £7

British 40-seat Air Liner No. 62X, 1939-41. £50

726 Modern Dinky ME10 1972-76. £

Four-engined Liner No. 62R, 1945-49. £20

Dinky Viking No. 70c, 1947-62. £7

Monospar No. 60E, 19 41. £7

DOLLS & TOYS

M Comet Racer No. 60G,
945-49.   £20

Hawker Hurricane No. 62H,
1939-41.   £35

Ensign Air Liner No. 62P,
1938-41.   £40

'lying Boat Clipper III,
No. 60W, 1938-41. £45

Seaplane No. 700, 1945-49.
£10

Auro York No. 70A &
704, 1946-59.   £20

'airey Battle No. 60N,
937-41.   £40

Twin-engined Fighter
No. 70D, 1946-55. £10

Spitfire No. 62E, 1940-
41.   £40

161

P1B Lightning Fighter No. 737, 1959-68.
£8

Bristol 713 Helicopter No. 715, 1956-62.
£10

Flying Fortress No. 62G, 1939-41. £50

A post-war Empire Flying Boat, 1949. £20

Camouflaged Whitworth Ensign Liner No.
68A, 1940-41.   £55

Sea Vixen No. 738 Naval Fighter, 1960-65.
£14

Modern Dinky Phantom 730, 1972-76. £7

Vickers Viking No. 70C, 1947-62. £7

DEL AIRCRAFT

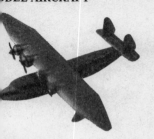

Four-engined Flying Boat, No. 60W, 1945-
49.   £15

French Meccano Air France Viscount No.
60E, 1957-60.   £35

Westland Sikorsky S.51 Helicopter, 1957-
52.   £8

Gloster Javelin No. 735, 1956-66.   £7

Ensign No. 62P, 1938-41.   £40

Nord Noratlas No 804, 1960-64.   £100

Vautoor No. 60B, French Issue, 1957-63.
                                              £20

Bloch 220, No. 64BZ, French made Dinky,
sold in U.K., 1939-40.   £45

MODEL BUILDINGS

A 19th century wooden and papier-mache butcher's shop, several pieces marked Germany, 12 x 6in.   £235

A Peek Freans biscuit tin 'Castle' made of four different sections, manufactured by Huntley Bourne & Stevens, 1923.   £260

A large 20th century model bird house. £25

A late 19th century glazed and cased model of M. Osborne's — The Butcher's Shop, 46.5 x 43.5cm.   £750

A Crown illuminated Panorama optical toy theatre, illuminated by a candle mounted behind, 9½in. wide.   £180

Britain's Army Building No. 1739, circa 1940, a model of gunners' quarters.   £1,000

MODEL BUILDINGS

Early 20th century Bing lithographed tin garage, Germany, with key-wind open car and closed sedan type car, 5½in. and 6½in.
£250

A Victorian Christmas cracker house.   £20

Wooden and paper toy theatre, manufactured for F. A. O. Schwartz Toys, circa 1885, 25 x 25in.   £66

A wooden and paper lithograph stable, circa 1875, 24 x 15 x 12in.   £200

American wooden miniature store, 9 x 13½ x 20½in., circa 1910.   £200

A model of a hall with marquetry floor dividing at the landing into stairs on either side going up to a galleried landing, 26in. wide.   £300

An exhibition standard 3in. scale model of
the Savage horse-drawn Electric Light Engine
No. 357, built by C. J. Goulding, Newport,
27 x 47in.   £2,800

An engineered model enclosed compound generating set, 13½ x 22in.
                                        £320

An early 20th century model single cylinder
surface condensing 'A' frame beam engine,
19½ x 24in.   £1,700

A Stuart Major Beam engine, cylinder, 2¼ x
4in., on wood stand in glazed case.   £510

A detailed steam driven model of a Bengali
Die Mixing plant, built by A. Sare, Northleach,
measurements overall 18½ x 24in.   £700

A finely engineered and well presented model
'M E', centre pillar beam engine, built by
K. R. F. Kenworthy, measurements overall
13 x 17½in.   £800

MODEL ENGINES

An early 20th century single cylinder horizontal mill engine, complete with mahogany
lagged brass bound cylinder, 2½ x 3in. £260

An early 18th century tinplate and cast-
iron model single horizontal cylinder gas
engine by Bing, 10 x 16in.   £600

An exhibition standard model of the three
cylinder compound surface condensing
vertical reversing marine engine fitted to
the Cunard Liner S.S. 'Servia' and modelled
by Thos. Lowe, 1907, 14½ x 12½in. £3,500

A fine contemporary late 19th century small,
full size, single cylinder horizontal mill engine,
measurements overall 18 x 25in.   £650

A model of an early 20th century twin
cylinder horizontal mill engine, complete
with mahogany lagged copper bound
cylinders, 2½ x 5in.   £480

A model of a three cylinder horizontal
reversing stationary engine, built by W.
G. Duggan, Benton and D. Ash. £450

MODEL ENGINES

Engineering model of an inclined compound surface paddle engine, 16½in. wide.   £1,400

An early single vertical cylinder open crank gas engine, probably American, 24 x 9in.   £190

A model Stuart triple expansion vertical reversing marine engine built by G. B. Houghton, Rochester, 7 x 8¾in.   £650

A well presented approx. 1:20 scale model of the Weatherhill Pit Winding Engine of 1833, built by W. K. Walsam, Hayes, 19 x 14½in.   £600

Late 19th century model of the three cylinder compound vertical surface condensing mill engine 'Asia', 16¼ x 13¼in. £1,900

An early 19th century small full size single cylinder six pillar beam engine, 31 x 34in   £900

A 1:20 scale brass model of the Fenton, Murray & Wood 6 N.H.P. underlever beam engine of 1806 built by G. L. Dimelow, Ashton-under-Lyne, 9¾ x 9¼in.   £600

An horizontal cylinder stationary steam engine, built by Negelin & Hubner, 28 x 64in.   £500

A contemporary early 19th century brass and wrought iron single cylinder six pillar beam engine, built by Chadburn Bros., Sheffield, 19 x 19¼in.   £2,000

MODEL ENGINES

An ingenious and well presented model steam driven Stone Sawing Plant, built by R. J. Sare, Northleach, 13½ x 24½in. £320

A finely engineered model twin cylinder compound undertype stationary steam engine built to the designs of A. H. Greenly, by P. C. Kidner, London, 14½ x 24½in. £1,500

A 1:12 scale model of a six horse-power pyramidical columned condensing rotative beam engine built by Messrs Fenton Murray & Co., circa 1810, 12 x 15in. £420

An exhibition standard model of the three cylinder compound surface condensing vertical reversing marine engine, fitted to S.S. 'Servia', and modelled by T. Lowe, 1907, 14½ x 12½in. £4,000

A live steam, spirit fired tinplate vertical steam engine, by Bing, circa 1928, 12½in. high, in original box. £99

A well presented model single cylinder vertical reversing stationary engine, built from Clarkson castings, 17½ x 9¾in. £700

An Exhibition Standard model of a single cylinder overcrank stationary engine, by A. Mount, London. £320

A late 19th century full size four-pillar twin-cylinder compound vertical reversing launch engine, 31½ x 24in. £1,700

An unusual model of a steam driven 19th century twin bore Deep Well Engine House and Pump, built by R. J. Sare, Northleach, 16½ x 18½in. £200

169

MODEL SHIPS

An early 20th century American steamship model, diorama scene in mahogany case, 48in. wide.   £465

Mid 19th century English sailor-made half-block ship model of a paddle steamer, 30in. wide.   £460

Mid 19th century shipping diorama, depicting the three-masted clipper 'Solway', together with a fishing smack, English, 39in. wide.   £550

Mid 19th century English sailor-made half-block model of a clipper, 34in. wide.   £300

A 1/24 scale fully planked electric powered model of the Herring Drifter 'Supernal', built by G. Wrigley, 1979/80 from drawings by R. Neville, 24 x 24in.   £1,430

A 1:48 scale fibreglass, wood and metal, electric-powered model of the coastal cargo ship S.S. Talacre of Liverpool, built by R. H. Phillips, 13 x 33in.   £440

An exhibition standard 'One Metre' class steam boat 'Papua', BH 19, built by A. Broad, Bromley, 8 x 40in.   £330

A well detailed wood and metal static display model of the Leander class frigate H.M.S. Aurora, Pennant No. F10, stand 14 x 16in.   £605

ODEL SHIPS

A wooden framed working model of a single screwing boat 'The Swift', circa 1904, Greenock, 32½in. long. £240

A shipbuilder's model of Lord Ashburton's steam yacht 'Venetia', Scottish, 1893, 67½in. long. £7,150

An English mid 19th century sailor-made shipping diorama, 30½in. wide. £300

A mid 19th century sailor-made model of the coaster 'Susan Vittery', English, 29½in. long. £500

A live steam spirit-fired wooden model of the paddle tug 'Alert' of Yarmouth, 21 x 39in. £1,595

Late 19th century carved and painted model of the 'William Tapscot', in a glass and mahogany case, 38in. long. £995

A builder's mirror backed half model of the schooner rigged steam yacht 'Rona', built for A. H. E. Wood Esq., by David and William Henderson & Co., 1893/4 to the order of Thomas and Campbell, designed by G. L. Watson & Co., 10 x 71in. £3,600

A builder's model of the single screw cargo ship M.V. 'Deerwood' of London, built 1955 by Wm. Pickersgill & Sons Ltd., for Wm. France, Fenwick & Co. Ltd., 12½ x 53in. £1,000

MODEL SHIPS

A 20th century American model of the extreme clippership 'Cutty Sark', on a walnut base, fitted in a glass case. £964

A contemporary early 19th century French prisoner of war bone and horn model man o war reputed to be the French ship of the lin 'Redoubtable' of 74 guns, 20½ x 26¾in. £8,000

Late 18th century prisoner-of-war carved ivory ship, with rigging and thirty-four gun ports, Europe, 13½in. long. £583

A planked and rigged model of a Royal Nava Cutter built by I. H. Wilkie, Sleaford, 36 x 42in. £35

A planked and framed fully rigged model of the Royal Naval armed brig H.M.S. 'Grasshopper' of circa 1806, built by R. Cartwright, Plymouth, 32 x 41in. £650

Early 19th century prisoner-of-war bone model of a ship-of-the-line, 7¾in. long. £2,328

MODEL SHIPS

A 20th century American model of a fishing schooner, 'Kearsar', fitted in a glass case, 33½in. long. £682

A 19th century three-masted ship model, sails furled, approx. 36in. long. £364

A detailed ¼in.:1ft. model of a twelve gun brig of circa 1840 built to the plans of H. A. Underhill by M. J. Gebhard, Tottenham, 36 x 47in. £3,000

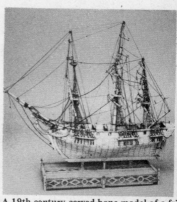

A 19th century carved bone model of a frigate, probably French, 16½in. long. £2,248

An early 19th century French prisoner-of-war bone model of a ship-of-the-line, 8½in. long. £1,846

Early 19th century prisoner-of-war bone model of a First Class ship-of-the-line, 21in. long. £7,226

MODEL SHIPS

A tinplate model liner, entitled 'The Queen Mary', probably German, circa 1930, 29in. long. £700

A Marklin tinplate and clockwork warship, H.M.S. Albion, 21in. long. £600

JEP: No. 3, clockwork streamline speedboat painted in pale blue and cream with driver, 36cm. long. £50

Early 20th century Walbert lithographed tin wind-up ferry boat, 13¾in. long. £138

Fleischmann tinplate clockwork model of a two-funelled ocean liner, 10½in. long. £150

A Bing repainted three-funnel liner with clockwork mechanism, 14¾in. long, circa 1925. £385

An early Carette carpet toy tinplate sailboat, with fly-wheel mechanism, German, circa 1905, 11¾in. long. £180

Dinky pre-war set No. 50, 'Ships of the British Navy', together with five other warships and 'Famous Liners'. £165

A late 19th/early 20th century ships model of a harbour dredger, 78in. long. £900

'Unterseeboot', a painted metal submarine, by Bing, circa 1902, 17¾in. long. £605

MODEL SHIPS

A Falk tinplate painted clockwork battle-ship, HMS Invincible, 37cm. long. £420

Fleischmann, tinplate clockwork liner No. 67, 51cm. long. £800

An early painted metal gun-boat with clock-work mechanism, by Bing, circa 1904, 10½in. long. £220

Tin clockwork steamboat, probably Gebruder Bing, Germany, 1920's, 32in. long. £1,400

A hand enamelled 'New Orleans Paddle Wheeler', probably by Dent, U.S.A., circa 1903, 10½in. long. £400

A Hess printed and painted tinplate toy of Dreadnought, with clockwork mechanism, circa 1911, 8½in. long. £60

A painted wood waterline dreadnought, probably by Carette, circa 1904, 5in. long, in original instruction box. £308

A painted tinplate river paddle steamer with clockwork mechanism, 11in. long, by Uebelacker, Nuremberg, circa 1902. £495

A painted tin wind-up tanker, by J. Fleisch-mann, Germany, 1950's, 19in. long. £155

A tinplate model of a three-funnel ocean liner, with clockwork mechanism operating two propellers, by Bing, circa 1920, 15½in. long. £800

175

MODEL SHIPS

Early 20th century shipbuilder's model of
the cargo vessel 'Nailsea Manor' built by
Bartram & Sons Ltd. of Sunderland, 54in.
long.   **£1,980**

A builder's mirror back half model of the
single screw cargo ship 'Persistence', 15 x
49¼in. overall.   **£3,300**

A 1:100 scale model of the Le Havre Pilot
Boat 'Henriette', pennant No. H2, of 1866,
built by M. Deveral, Folkestone, 8 x 8in.
                                          £220

A builder's 3/16in.:1ft. scale model of H.M.S.
'Transport Ferry No. 3016', built for the
Royal Navy by R. & W. Hawthorn, Leslie &
Co. Ltd., Hebburn-on-Tyne, 1945, 16 x 63½in.
                                          £3,000

A fully planked un-rigged boxwood model
of H.M.S. Circe, circa 1875, built by T. Wake,
Stockwood, 5 x 17in.   **£71**

Late 19th century shipbuilder's half-block
model of a Barquentine 'Sound of Jura',
English, 67in. long.   **£1,200**

An exhibition standard 1:72 scale planked and
fully rigged model of the French frigate 'La
Venus' of circa 1782, built by P. M. di Gragnano
Naples, 31 x 44in.   **£4,500**

A boxwood, lime and walnut model of
'H.M.S. Endeavour', made by Brian
Hinchcliffe, English, modern, 30in. long.
                                          £5,500

MODEL SHIPS

A contemporary model of Sir Henry Segrave's record breaking power boat Miss England, length of vessel 12in., in glazed case. £340

Early 20th century shipbuilder's model of the turret deck steamer 'Duffryn Manor', English, 44in. long, in glazed mahogany case. £2,200

Late 19th century English shipbuilder's half-block model of a yacht, 24in. long. £350

A painted tinplate model of an early 4-funnel torpedo boat, by Bing, circa 1912, 16in. long. £300

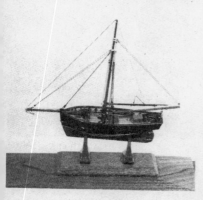

A 1:100 scale model of a Trouville trawler of circa 1866, built by M. Deveral, Folkestone, 6 x 6½in. £220

Late 19th century possibly builder's model of the fully rigged model of a yawl believed to be the 'Constance' of 1885, built for C. W. Prescott-Westcar by A. Payne & Sons, Southampton and designed by Dixon Kemp, 28 x 35¾in. £4,000

A half-block model of the Coaster 'S.S. Ardnagrena', Scottish, built by G. Brown & Co., Greenock, 1908, 42in. wide. £935

Early 20th century model of the Clyde steamer 'Duchess of Fife', made by N. S. Forbes, 54in. long. £2,860

177

MODEL SHIPS

Late 19th century model of a fore-and-aft schooner 'Swallow', 55in. long, on stand.   £484

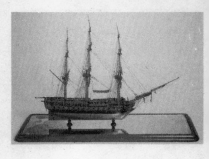

Early 19th century prisoner-of-war box-wood model of the 48-gun Ship-of-the-Line 'Glory', 20 x 28in.   £13,200

A 19th century model of a Gloucester fishing schooner, 'Columbia', fully rigged with wooden sails, 20.3/8in. long.   £545

A fully planked and rigged model of a 72-gun man-o'-war, built by P. Rumsey, Bosham, 26 x 37in.   £1,650

A carved and painted model of the 'Royal Ark', by J. R. Whittemore, on a molded wooden base, 43in. long.   £1,280

Early 19th century prisoner-of-war bone model of a frigate, 7in. long, under glass dome.   £990

DEL SHIPS

ully planked and rigged bone and wood
del of a topsail schooner built by P. Rumsey,
sham, 10 x 14in.   £418

An exhibition standard 1:75 scale fully planked
and rigged model of the French 60 gun man-of-
war 'Le Protecteur' of circa 1760, built by P.
M. di Gragnano, Naples, 31 x 38in.   £5,000

1:60 scale model of the late 18th century
rench Ceremonial Galley 'Reale de France',
uilt by J. Cherrill, Weybridge, 25 x 42in.
                                     £900

An exhibition standard 1:384 scale model of
H.M.S. Rattlesnake, circa 1781, built by J.
Evans, Whyteleaf.   £1,760

A finely carved and detailed contemporary
early 19th century boxwood model of the
28-gun man-o'-war H.M.S. Nelson, 1 3½ x
10½in.   £9,350

A contemporary model of a Bristol slaver,
English, circa 1810, 45in. long.   £1,540

MODEL SHIPS

Mid 19th century half-block model of a clipper with carved wooden sails, 24in. long, in glazed wall case. £350

Model of a steam-driven day yacht 'Lady Eleanor', 59½in. long, with stand below. £616

A well detailed live steam, spirit fired, radio controlled, fully planked and framed model of the Barry Pilot Cutter 'Chimaera' of circa 1918, built by Marvon Models, Doncaster, 24½ x 47in. £1,000

A contemporary mid 19th century model the Paddle Steamer 'Atlanta', 18½ x 41in. £4,9

A Bing battleship 'H.M.S. Powerful', German, circa 1912, 29in. long. £935

A wood and metal electric powered model o a Watson Type self-righting lifeboat, circa 1925. 24in. long, by Bassett-Lowke. £32

A 1/8in.:1ft. scale builder's model of the single screw steam newsprint carrier 'Sarah Bowater' of London, built 1955 by Denny Bros., Dumbarton for the Bowater Paper Corporation Ltd., 12 x 52in. £2,000

A display model of the motor tanker 'Londo Glory', built by Messrs. Sir James Laing & Sons Ltd., Sunderland for London & Oversea Freighters Ltd. Yard No. 793, 1952 and mod led for the builders by I. R. Amis Ltd. Londo 7 x 31in. £70

wood waterline model of the R.M.S.
dinburgh Castle built by Bassett-Lowke, the
ip 30in. long, in glazed case. £400

Bassett Lowke three-funnel torpedo boat,
circa 1920, 54in. long on stand. £400

model of the single screw tug 'Devonmoor',
uilt by J. Gregory, Plymouth, 18 x 34in.
£990

Modern scale model of the barque 'Harriet
McGregor', with copper-sheathed wooden
hull, 26in. long. £220

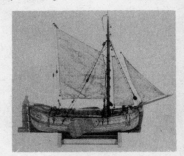

Early 20th century model gun-boat Chinese,
9½in. long, on carved wood simulated sea.
£418

Early 20th century English model of a barge
with detailed fittings, 25in. long. £550

model of a paddle steamer 'Caledonian',
nglish, circa 1900, 56in. long. £550

An exhibition standard ¾in.:1ft. scale model of
the steam yacht 'Turbinia', as developed to 1895
and modelled by A. Broad, Bromley, 18½ x 77in.
£1,300

A rake of three fine gauge 1 Great Western Railway twin bogie passenger coaches, by G. £300

A gauge 1 clockwork model of the London and and North Western Railway 4-6-2 'Bowen-Cooke' tank locomotive No. 2663, in black livery, by Marklin for Bassett-Lowke, circa 1913. £850

An early Bing 2½in. gauge II live steam spirit fired Midland Railway 4-4-0 locomotive, with a six-wheel tender and a six-wheel carriage, the locomotive 14in. long, circa 1902-06. £660

A gauge 0 clockwork model of the North Boarder Railway 4-4-0 pannier tank locomotive, by Bing for Bassett-Lowke, and a Bassett-Lowke clockwork mechanism. £150

A fine gauge 1 clockwork model of the London and North Western Railway 4-4-2 'Precursor Tank' locomotive No. 44, in black livery, by Bing for Bassett-Lowke, circa 1810. £380

A rake of three gauge 1 Midland Railway twin bogie passenger cars, including two first class coaches and a 3rd class brake car, by Bing for Bassett-Lowke, circa 1927. £360

Two gauge 1 Great Northern Railway, teak, 1st/3rd class twin bogie passenger cars, Nos. 2875, by Marklin, circa 1925. £260

A gauge 3 live- steam spirit-fired model of the London and South Western Railway 4-4-0 locomotive and tender, by Bing for Bassett-Lowke, circa 1904. £2,800

A contemporary mid 19th century 4½in. gauge brass model of the 2-2-2 locomotive 'Apollo' of 1844 built by Franklin & Co., Manchester, 9¾ x 14¼in. £3,200

A Marklin 3RE 20 volts 4-4-0 LMS locomotive and four wheeler tender, the first/third class carriages and brake van, Bing controller. £460

DEL TRAINS

wo gauge 0 C.I.W.L. twin bogie passenger
baches, restaurant car, Ref. No. 1746/GJ1,
d sleeping car, Ref. No. 1747/GJ1, by
arklin.   £75

A 3½in. gauge model of the London and North
Eastern Railway Class V2 2-6-2 locomotive and
tender 'Green Arrow' built by A. Ficker, Rad-
lett, 10½ x 53in.   £1,500

5in. gauge model of the London and North
stern Railway Class J39 0-6-0 locomotive
d tender No. 2934, built by K. Edge, Peter-
rough, 13¾ x 59in.   £2,500

A Bing spirit fired 0-4-0 LNWR locomotive and
tender No. 1942 with separated lamps and a
Bing gauge 1 signal.   £280

gauge 1 (3-rail) electric model of a Contin-
ntal 4-4-0 locomotive and tender, by Bing,
irca 1910.   £320

A gauge 0 (3-rail) electric model of the 0-4-0
locomotive, Ref. No. RF66/12920, by
Marklin.   £240

7¼in. gauge model of the Hunslet 0-4-0 con-
ctor's locomotive designed by M. R. Harrison
d modelled by J. Maxted, Ramsgate, measure-
nts overall 33½ x 98in.   £2,800

'Juliet', a 3½in. gauge live steam coal fired
0-4-0 tank locomotive, together with a trailer,
20in. long overall.   £200

gauge 1 London and North Western Railway
vin bogie 3rd class brake car, by Bing for
assett-Lowke, circa 1922.   £130

Pre-war French Factory 16Z diesel streamlined
train by Dinky.   £340

MODEL TRAINS

A Bing for Bassett-Lowke gauge O clockwork model of the LMS 4-4-0 'Compound' locomotive and tender No. 1053 'George the Fifth',
£110

A Bassett-Lowke gauge 0, 3-rail, electric model of the GWR 2-6-0 'Mogul' locomotive and tender No. 4331, in original paintwork.
£660

A gauge 0 clockwork model of the LNER 4-4-0 No. 2 special locomotive and tender No. 201, 'The Bramham Moor', by Hornby.
£660

A 4in. gauge LMS model tank engine, heavy goods type, steam driven, on oak stand.
£1,200

A Hornby pre-war gauge 0 clockwork No. 2 tank goods set, in original box, and an M1 locomotive.
£308

A 7¼in. gauge model of the Great Eastern Railway 0-4-0 locomotive No. 710, steel boiler with 7in. barrel and superheater, cylinders 2.1/8in. x 3¾in., driving wheels 8in. diam.
£2,300

A Bing gauge 0 clockwork model of the LNER 4-6-0 locomotive and tender No. 4472, 'Flying Fox', in original paintwork.
£330

An early gauge 1 (3-rail) electric (4v) model of the LNWR 4-4-0 'Compound' locomotive and tender No. 2663, 'George The Fifth', by Marklin, circa 1912.
£495

Marklin, gauge 1, clockwork 4-4-0 locomotive
nd tender No. 1031.   £420

Marklin for Gamages, gauge 1, clockwork
0-4-0 G.N.R. locomotive and tender No. 294.
£320

Hornby pre-war gauge 0 No. 0 vans, including
two milk, ventilated refrigerator, perishable,
meat; two No. 2 high capacity wagons and a
Bing LNWR open wagon.   £242

Marklin gauge 1 (e-rail) electric model of a
Continental 4-4-0 'Compound' locomotive
and six-wheeled tender No. 65/13041.
£220

A Stevens's model dockyard, 3¼in. gauge
live-steam spirit fired brass model of an
early 2-2-0 locomotive, in original box,
circa 1900.   £209

A Hornby pre-war gauge 0 No. 2 tank
Passenger train set, in original box.
£462

Hornby No. 00 train, early 1920's clockwork
in printed MR locomotive and tender No. 483,
with key.   £85

Bing, gauge 1, clockwork 0-4-0 locomotive
and tender No. 48, (unnamed).   £280

A 7¼in. gauge model of the Great Western Railway 15XX Class 0-6-0 Pannier tank locomotive No. 1500, rebuilt by F. West, Lee Green, 21 x 55in. £5,000

A gauge 0 (3-rail) electric model of a Continental 4-6-2 'Pacific' locomotive and twin bogie tender, Ref. No. HR64/13020, by Marklin, circa 1930. £1,500

A gauge 0 live steam spirit-fired model of the S.E.C.R. steam railcar, by Carette, circa 1908. £1,000

A 3½in. gauge model of the 4-4-0 locomotive and tender No. 573 built to the designs of 'Virginia', 11½ x 45in. £900

A collection of the Great Western Railway coaching stock including the twin bogie full brake No. 188, the six wheel full brake No. 95 and the four wheel horsebox No. 88, painted by L. Goddard. £250

A 7mm. finescale two rail electric model of the London Midland and Scottish Railway Class 7P 4-6-2 locomotive and tender No. 6231 'Duchess of Athol' as built in 1938, the model by D. Jenkinson and painted by L. Goddard, 3¾ x 20½in. £750

A 7¼in. gauge model of the Great Western Railway 4-6-0 locomotive and tender No. 1011 'County of Chester' rebuilt and reboilered by F. West, 21¾ x 10in. £12,000

A gauge 0 (3-rail) electric model of a Continental Doll BLS electric engine, with overhead pantograph, by Bing, circa 1930. £200

A 5in. model of the London and North Eastern Railway Class A3 4-6-2 locomotive and tender No. 2568 'Sceptre' built by K. Edge, 1975, 15 x 75in. £3,200

An exhibition standard 5in. gauge model of the William Dean diagram 21 Brake Composite twin bogie passenger coach No. 3391 of 1897, 13 x 57in. £1,800

A detailed exhibition standard 5in. gauge
model of the British Railways Class 7 4-6-2
locomotive and tender No. 70000 'Britannia',
4 x 76in.   £6,000

5in. gauge model of the Great Western Railway 4-6-0 locomotive and tender No. 6011
'King James I' built by K. Edge, 15 x 73in.
                                             £5,200

A 3½in. gauge model of the London and
North Eastern Railway Class B1 4-6-0 locomotive and tender No. 8301 'Springbok'
built by T. Dyche, York, 10¼ x 47in.
                                             £1,700

5in. gauge model of the Great Western Railway 0-6-0 Pannier tank locomotive No. 9716
built to the designs of Pansy, 13½ x 34in.
                                             £1,400

gauge 0 clockwork model of the London
Midland and Scottish Railway 4-4-0 locomotive and six-wheel tender No. 5320 'George
', by Bing for Bassett-Lowke.   £150

A 7mm. finescale two rail electric model of
the London Brighton and South Coast Railway Stroudley Class D1 0-4-2 side tank locomotive No. 351, built by B. Miller, 3¾ x 8¾in.
                                             £420

A 5in. gauge model of the Great Northern Railway Stirling Single 4-2-2 locomotive and tender No. 9 built by H. Bannister, Burton-on-
Trent, 15 x 58in.   £2,800

A 5in. gauge model of the London Midland
and Scottish Railway re-built Scot Class 4-6-0
locomotive and tender No. 6154 'The Hussar'
built by K. Edge, Peterborough, 15½ x 70in.
                                             £3,000

A 7mm. finescale two rail electric model of
the British Railways (ex L.M.S.) 0-6-0 'Jinty'
side tank locomotive No. 47469, built by M.
H. C. Models, Bolton, 3½ x 8½in.   £420

An exhibition standard 5in. gauge model of
the Great Western Railway Dean Single 4-2-2
locomotive and tender No. 3012 'Great
Western', 14 x 61in.   £7,000

A 7¼in. gauge model of the Great Western
Railway Armstrong Class 4-4-0 locomotive and
tender No. 8 'Gooch', built by T. Childs,
Churchill, 20¼ x 88in. £7,000

An exhibition standard 5in. gauge model of the
Great Western Railway River Class 2-4-0 locomotive and tender No. 69 'Avon' as running in
1906, built from builder's drawings and photographs by R. W. Gale, Newport, 14¼ x 53¼in.
£7,500

A well engineered 3½in. gauge model of the
Great Western Railway County class 4-6-0 loco-
motive and tender No. 1022 'County of
Northampton', 10 x 47in. £1,500

A 3½in. gauge model of the British Railways
Class 7 4-6-2 locomotive and tender No. 7001
'Oliver Cromwell, built by H. C. Luckhurst,
Oxley, 10¼ x 52½in. £2,00

A 5in. gauge model of the London Midland
and Scottish Railway Class 2F 0-6-0 side tank
locomotive No. 11270, 13 x 27½in. £1,900

A 7¼in. gauge model of the London Midland
and Scottish Railway Class 2F 0-6-0 side tank
locomotive No. 11270, built by C. Ottaway,
Chippenham, 18½ x 41in. £4,50

A 3½in. gauge model of the Southern Railway
0-4-2 side tank locomotive No. 2036, built to
the designs of Juliet by M. Darlow, 1972 —
10 x 21in. £450

A Hornby gauge 0 (3-rail) electric model of
the No. 1 LNER 0-4-0 special locomotive an
tender, original paintwork, (loco in original
box). £280

DEL TRAINS

well engineered 2½in. gauge model of the
London Midland and Scottish Railway 4-4-0
locomotive and tender No. 1000, built to the
designs of Eagle by G. Ward, 8 x 31in.
£400

An exhibition standard 5in. gauge model of the
Great Northern Railway Stirling Single 4-2-2
locomotive and tender No. 53, built from works
drawings and photographs by J. S. Richardson,
Halifax, 14 x 56in.
£5,000

finely detailed 7mm. finescale two rail electric
model of the Deutches Bundesbahn 144 Bo Bo
ss electric outline locomotive No. E44070
ilt by Hego Modellbahn for the Nuremburg
y Fair, 1976, 4 x 13½in.
£500

A mid 19th century live steam spirit fired 4¾in.
gauge brass model of the 2-2-2 locomotive and
tender 'Express', built by Steven's Model Dockyard, 11¾ x 30in.
£2,100

ine Marklin gauge 1 clockwork model of the
& SCR 4-4-2 'Atlantic' tank locomotive
, 22, in original paintwork, with lamps, circa
20 (1 loose bogie).
£2,000

A gauge 1 (3-rail) electric model of the G.N.R.
0-4-0 side tank locomotive No. 112, in
original paintwork by Bing for Bassett-Lowke
(lacks 3 buffers).
£260

n exhibition standard 5in. gauge model of the
reat Western Railway Armstrong Class 4-4-0
comotive and tender No. 14, 'Charles
aunders', built by P. J. Rich, Rhiwderin, 14
62in.
£10,200

A fine contemporary late 19th century 3¼in.
gauge brass and steel spirit fired model 4-2-0
locomotive and tender, built by H. J. Wood,
London, 8½ x 21½in.
£650

MODEL TRAINS

Set No. 1771RW, gauge 0 No. 1681 Hudson
type locomotive 2-6-4, 8-wheel 1936 version
tender and three pullmans, American Flyer
Lines.   £462

A gauge 1 Bing locomotive 4-4-0 with 6-wheel
tender, circa 1915.   £1,002

A Hornby O gauge 'Bramham Moor' 4-4-0
clockwork locomotive and tender, finished
in LNER apple green, with brass nameplate
to each side, circa 1925.   £350

A Voltamp gauge 2 trolley No. 2123, 0-4-4-0,
circa 1913.   £2,159

Carette green locomotive, 2-2-0, 4-wheel
tender, alcohol burner, together with an olive
4-wheel baggage car, circa 1905.   £655

A Hornby O gauge 4-4-2 electric locomotive
'Lord Nelson', finished in Southern region,
together with an SR tender, circa 1900.   £22?

A 7¼in. gauge model of the North Eastern
Railway Class G5 0-4-4 side tank locomotive No.
505, built by D. W. Horsfall, Northowram, 20½
x 52½in.   £2,000

A 5in. gauge model of the Great Western Railway 57XX Class 0-6-0 pannier tank locomotive No. 5702, built by C. G. Balding, Bideford
13½ x 34in.   £1,60?

A 3½in. gauge live-steam 2-4-0 locomotive,
27½in. long, circa 1880's.   £1,200

Hornby gauge O clockwork 4-4-0
locomotive 'Bramham Moor', No. 20,
with six-wheeled tender.   £200

▶DEL TRAINS

'Washington Special', No. 385E locomotive ith tender and cars, circa 1934. £1,387

A 2½in. gauge live-steam coal-fired engineered model of a 2-6-2 Pannier Tank locomotive, 24in. long, modern. £1,500

gauge 1 (3-rail) electric model of the Great orthern Railway 4-4-2 'Atlantic' locomotive d tender No. 1442, by Bing for Bassett-Lowke. £650

A Bassett-Lowke gauge O electric 'Flying Scotsman', English, circa 1935, finished in British Railways Caledonian blue and black lined cream. £500

An exhibition standard 5in. gauge model of the British Railways Dukedog Class 4-4-0 locomotive and tender No. 9014, built by I. P. Watson, 14 x 60in. £5,000

A late 19th century 3¾in. gauge spirit fired brass model of the Great Northern Railway Stirling 2-4-0 locomotive and tender No. 152, built by H. J. Wood, London, 10¼ x 35in. £1,200

A rake of four gauge 1 Great Northern Railway eak passenger carriages, all by Marklin, circa 925. £300

A Marklin gauge 1 tinplate bogie kaiserwagen, German, circa 1901, 11in. long. £600

Stevens & Brown painted tin train, 'Thunderer' lack and red engine, green tender and two yel- ow passenger cars, America, 1870's, engine 7in. ong. £2,300

Hornby gauge O clockwork 4-4-2 tank locomotive, No. 2221, finished in G.W.R. green and black lined gold. £70

MODEL TRAINS

No. 5 thin rim locomotive lettered 'B & O R.R.', circa 1907.   £1,465

Marklin 4-4-0 live steam spirit-fired gauge 'one' locomotive, German, circa 1915. £350

Exhibition standard 4mm. scale electric model of the Metropolitan Railway tank locomotive No. 106, 6½in. long.   £400

A gauge 1 clockwork model of the Great Northern Railway 2-4-0 side tank locomotive, by Marklin. £450

A gauge 1 clockwork model of an 0-4-0 Peckett saddle tank locomotive No. 204, by Carette for Bassett-Lowke.   £350

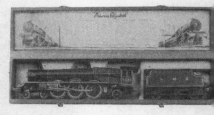

Hornby, 3.R.E. Princess Elizabeth and tender, boxed.   £1,100

A 3½in. gauge copper and brass spirit fired 2-4-0 locomotive, No. 715, English, circa 1880's, 17¼in. long. £1,100

A gauge 1 clockwork model of the London Tilbury and Southend Railway 4-4-2 side tank locomtovie No. 10 'Grays'.   £650

ODEL TRAINS

A Bassett-Lowke gauge O clockwork
0-4-4 tank locomotive, 'Shallow Horse',
No. 109. £460

A 3½in. gauge model of the old
Canterbury & Whitstable Railway
'Invicta', £400

A 6½in. gauge 1¼in. scale electrified display
model of the Glasgow and Garnkirk Railway
Robert Stephenson 'Four Coupled Planet'
0-4-0 locomotive and tender of 1831, 15 x
36in. £2,000

Late 19th century boxed Marklin wind-up
train set, sold by F.A.O. Schwartz, New
£1,272

One of two Marklin gauge '1' tinplate passenger coaches, hand-painted, German, circa
1902. £1,210

A 7mm. finescale two-rail electric
model of the London and North
Eastern Railway 'Coffee Pot' 0-4-0
saddle tank locomotive No. 7230. £400

A gauge 1 clockwork model of an
0-4-0 Peckett saddle tank locomotive
No. 810, by Carette for Bassett-Lowke.
£300

A 5in. gauge model of the Great Western
Railway 'Metro' 2-4-0 side tank locomotive.
£1,500

MODEL VEHICLES

An exhibition standard 2in. scale model of
the Clayton Undertype Articulated wagon,
built by E. W. D. Sheppard.   £1,500

A Bing clockwork threshing machine, circa
1905.   £660

An Exhibition Standard 2in. scale model
of the Wallis & Stevens 'Advance' Road
Roller, built by S. Jackson. (Christie's S.
$5,250 £3,500

A 3in. scale model of a Wallis & Stevens
'Simplicity' Road Roller, built by D. G.
Edwards, 1980, 24¾ x 35in.   1£950

A well engineered 3in. scale model of a Suffolk
Dredging tractor, built by C. E. Thorn,
27 x 30in.   £480

A scale model of a Ferguson TE20 tractor and
plough, 15¾in. long overall.   £285

Lesney Massey Harris 745D tractor. £120

An approx. 4in. scale Foden type twin
cylinder overtype two speed steam lorry,
built by A. Groves, Watford, 1937 and
restored by M. Williams at the British
Engineerium, Hove, 1983, 36½ x 88in.
£5,000

MODELS

Marx, Armoured Floating Tank Transporter, boxed.   £45

A large scale model of the British airship R100-G-FAAV, 10ft. long, with tower, 4ft.   £1,500

A 19th century circus wagon, 28in. overall, wagon 16 x 7½in.   £115

Early 20th century miniature Eskimo model of dogsled and team, wooden sled, and four rabbit skin covered papier mache dogs, sled 12.3/8in. long.   £287

A gauge 1 signals gantry, with four signals, oil fired lamps and ladders on both sides, by Bing, circa 1910, 21in. high.   £440

An early 20th century wood model of the 1860 horse-drawn goods wagon owned by Carter Paterson & Co, London and Suburban Express Carriers, 17in. long.   £320

German tinplate model of a coalmine.   £85

A Louis Marx tinplate 'Main St.' Tramway, the loop track with overhead power pylons with trams and trucks moving between station and terminal, 24in. long.   £100

MONEY BANKS

A tinplate monkey mechanical bank, German, circa 1930, 6½in. high.   £300

Lion and Monkeys cast iron mechanical bank, Kyser & Rex Co., Pat. 1883, 10in. long.   £277

Organ and Monkey mechanical bank, patented 1882, 7¼in. high.   £227

A cast iron money bank of a golly, 15.5cm. high.   £100

'Trick Dog', a mechanical cast-iron moneybox, by J. & E. Stevens, circa 1888, 8¾ x 3in.   £330

Late 19th century American 'Uncle Sam' mechanical bank, by Shepard Hardware Co., 11½in. high.   £220

German 7.11/16in. Symphonion musical savings bank, 17½in. high, circa 1905.   £2,420

A cast iron novelty bank, by J. & E. Stevens Co., the building with front door opening to reveal a cashier, American, late 19th century.   £250

Late 19th century cast iron owl money bank.   £12

'Tammany Bank', a cast iron mechanical bank, the seated gentleman with articulated right arm, 5¾in. high, by J. and E. Stevens Co., circa 1875. £100

Late 19th century American cast-iron 'Trick Pony' mechanical bank, by Shepard Hardware Co., 7in. wide. £418

American late 19th century Stump Speaker cast-iron mechanical bank, 9¾in. high. £1,265

Stollwerck Bros. Post Savings-Bank', modelled as a chocolate dispenser, circa 1911, 6½in. high. £176

Stevens cast-iron Indian and Bear mechanical bank, Conn., circa 1875, 10.9/16in. long. £799

Late 19th century cast iron clown mechanical bank, 9½in. high. £400

Transvaal Moneybox', a mechanical cast-iron money-box of Paul Kruger. £143

Late 19th century American cast-iron 'Santa Claus' mechanical bank, 6in. high. £495

Late 19th century cast-iron organ bank, 7¼in. high. £500

MONEY BANKS

William Tell cast iron mechanical bank, J. & E. Stevens, Co., pat. 1896, 10.5/8in. long. £416

A cast iron 'Eagle and Eaglets' mechanical bank, by J. & E. Stevens, patented 1883, 6¾in. long. £280

'Bad Accident' cast iron mechanical bank, J. & E. Stevens, Co., 1891-1911 10.3/8in. long. £763

Late 19th century American cast-iron 'Punch & Judy' mechanical bank, by Shepard Hardware Co., 7½in. high. £462

A cast iron 'Always Did 'Spise a Mule' money bank, American, circa 1897, by J. Stevens & Co., 10in. long. £700

American late 19th century Paddy and the Pig cast-iron mechanical bank, 8in. high. £60

Late 19th century English cast-iron 'Giant in the Tower' mechanical bank, 9¼in. high. £2,420

'Artillery', a cast-iron money-box, with a moulded cannon, and a World War I tank, by Starkies, circa 1915, 10in. long. £154

Late 19th century American cast iron mechanical bank, 'Stump Speaker', 9½in. high £95

'World's Fair' cast iron mechanical bank, J. & E. Stevens, Co., pat. 1893, 8¼in. long. £416

A 20th century English cast-iron 'Dinah' mechanical bank, by John Harper & Co. Ltd., 6½in. high. £104

A mechanical cast iron money box, as a football player with articulated right leg, causing the player to shoot a coin into a goal and ring a bell, circa 1890, 10½in. long. £550

Late 19th century cast iron 'Speaking Dog' mechanical bank, by J. & E. Stevens Co., ?¼in. long. £800

'Bull Dog Bank' cast iron mechanical bank, J. & E. Stevens, Co., pat. 1880, 7½in. high. £347

A late 19th century cast iron 'Girl Skipping Rope' mechanical bank, 20cm. wide. £8,250

20th century Kenton cast iron flatiron building bank, America, 8¼in. high. £160

A cast iron two frogs mechanical bank, American, late 19th century, 8½in. long. £450

Late 19th century cast-iron Hall's Excelsior bank, American, 5¼in. high. £300

American late 19th century 'Artillery Bank' cast-iron mechanical bank, 8in. long. £250

'United States and Spain', a mechanical cast-iron money-box, by J. & E. Stevens, circa 1898, 8½ x 2½in. £1,210

Late 19th century Amer can cast-iron 'Negro and Shack' money bank, 4¼i long. £300

'I always did 'spise a mule' mechanical bank, by J. & E. Stevens, patented 1879, 8in. high. £189

Late 19th century American cast-iron leap frog mechanical bank, by Shepard Hardware Co., 7½in. wide. £308

'Jolly Nigger' metal mone bank. £6

Two frogs cast iron mechanical bank, J. & E. Stevens, Co., Pat. 1882, 8¾in. long. £434

German tinplate 'monkey' money bank with decorated base, 6½in. high. £100

'Chief Big Moon' cast iron mechanical bank, J. & E. Stevens, Co., pat. 1899, 10 long. £83

Pratt money box model-
ed as a chapel, inscribed
muel Townsend 1848,
cm. £420

An unusual tin 'Combination
Safe' money box. £20

A Prattware cottage money
box in the form of a two-
storeyed house with blue
tiled roof, 12.5cm. high.
£420

An unusual wind-up drum-
mer boy money box, 6in.
high. £40

Oliver Hardy money box,
late 1950's. £10

One of a pair of German
electroplated Britannia
metal 'porker' money
boxes, 13.7cm. long.
£300

A money box modelled as a
chapel, inscribed Salley Harper
Hougate March 16th 1845,
6¾in. high. £450

Red and black painted tin
money box in the shape of
a 'pillar box', circa 1930,
6½in. high. £40

Jgeha money box clock by
Buerer Spar, in enamelled
case. £100

MUSICAL TOYS

A small Victorian musical box, the top decorated with children playing, 6 x 4in.£45

20th century 'Jiving Jigger' musical drum, 4in. diam. £40

A tinplate toy gramophone, printed 'Made in Germany', 1930's, 8¼in. long. £60

Portable gramophone by Peter Pan now much sought after by collectors, circa 1920. £120

A Magic Disc phenakisticope optical toy with 8 discs, each 7in. diam., a viewing disc, 9in. diam., and a Fantascope disc, 5in. diam. £480

A German printed tinplate musical cathedral, printed marks DRGM, Made in Germany, 17.5cm. high. £70

NOAH'S ARKS

An Edwardian painted wooden model of a Noah's Ark, containing approx. 120 painted carved wooden animals, 56cm. long. £720

A painted wood Noah's Ark on wheels, with opening roof, door and windows, German, circa 1890, 31in. long. £209

A painted wood Noah's Ark, by Erzegebirge, Germany, circa 1870, 23¾in. long, approx. 205 animals. £935

Mid 19th century Bavarian Noah's Ark, 19in. long, complete with animals. £500

NOVELTIES

'No doubt my wife has something nice and warm for me this cold night'. £20

'If I could only get the door down, I should see them all for nothing'. £20

NOVELTY BOOKS

'Joey the Clown and his dog Spot',
by P. A. Purton.   £5

'See-Saw Margery Daw', Jigsaw Picture Book. £3

'Dan Dare's 'Anastasia' Jet Plane', by Wallis Rigby. £25

'Dean's Home Stencil Book, No. 1', by Dean &
Son, 1930's.   £5

'My First Jig-Puz Book', Five Jigsaws.
£30

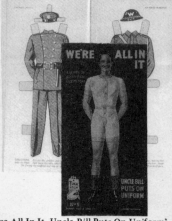

'We're All In It, Uncle Bill Puts On Uniform'. £8

NOVELTY BOOKS

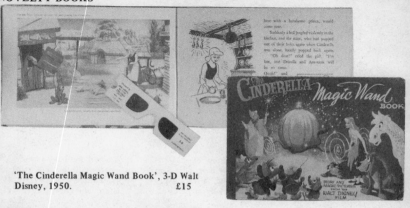

'The Cinderella Magic Wand Book', 3-D Walt
Disney, 1950.   £15

'Sewing Pictures' 1940's. £3

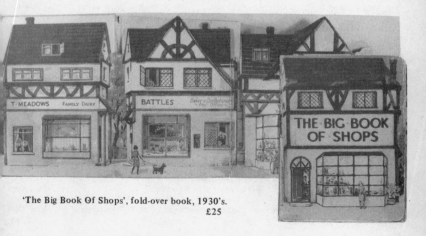

'The Big Book Of Shops', fold-over book, 1930's.
                    £25

OPTICAL TOYS

Rowsell's parlour grapho-
scope, folding table model,
base 23 x 12in., circa 1875.
£162

A zoetrope, the tinplate
painted drum on a woo-
den base with six paper
strips, 14in. high, circa
1880.   £247

A wood and brass magic
lantern with brass bound lens
and chimney with a slide
holder and a small quantity
of slides in wood box. £165

Rosewood stereo viewer,
table top, manufactured
by Alex. Becker, N.Y.,
circa 1859.   £325

An Ive's Kromskop colour
stereoscopic viewer, in wood
carrying case.   £700

A Le Praxinoscope optical
toy with shade and ten
picture strips, by Emile
Reynaud, drum with sellers
label.   £132

A small Zoetrope optical
toy on wood stand with
several picture strips, diam.
of drum 5¼in.   £100

A London Stereoscopic Co.
Brewster-pattern stereoscope
with brass mounted eye pieces,
in fitted rosewood box, 13in.
wide.   £380

A mutoscope in cast iron
octagonal shaped case,
electrically lit, 22in. high.
£715

EDAL CARS

An Austin A40 pedal car complete with operative electric headlamps, circa 1950. £400

Post war tinplate pedal car 'Austin Devon' with battery operated headlamps, 60in. long. £170

An early childs' pedal car by Chas. Boardman and Sons. £250

American child's pedal car, circa 1925, by Steelcraft, 36in. long. £250

An early Lines Bros. pedal car, the wooden body painted suede grey with sprung chassis, 39in. long. £550

A painted metal model of an Austin J40 Roadster pedal car, 64in. long, British, circa 1950. £750

Volkswagon 'Beetle' cabriolet with fibre glass white body, 5 h.p. Briggs & Straton engine, 6ft.6in. long. £1,000

Rare child-sized model of the Austin Seven racing car. £750

'Bookano Stories', 1940's. £25

'Hans Andersen's Fairy Stories', Bookano. £25   'Into Space with Ace Brave!', 1950's. £10

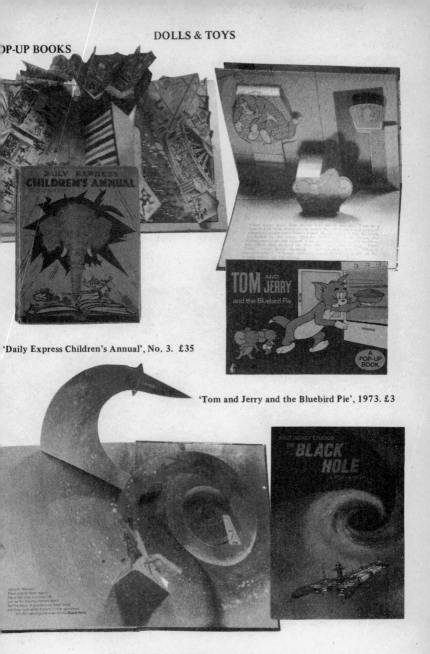

'Daily Express Children's Annual', No. 3. £35

'Tom and Jerry and the Bluebird Pie', 1973. £3

'The Black Hole', Walt Disney Studios, 1979. £5

POP-UP BOOKS

'ABC in Living Models', Bookano, 1930's. £25

'The Story of Jesus', Bookano, 1938. £10

'Prince Albert Driving His Favourites'. £12

'Album Victorianum'.   £18

1950's doll's pram with tin body and fabric hood. £30

A metal bodied Leeway pram with plastic interior. £45

950's Royal' pram with plywood body. £35

Wooden bodied doll's pram with vinyl interior and fabric hood. £30

Doll's pram with scroll and lattice wicker-work body, 30in. long. £55

Tri-ang doll's pram with metal body and plastic and fabric hood, 1960's. £25

PRAMS

Country style oak framed back to back
twin pram with brass hubs.   £180

A rare Bassinett two-handled double pram
with painted leather body, circa 1860. £250

A large 1960's Silver Cross pram with metal
body and fabric and leatherette upholstery.
                                     £35

Silver Cross 1930's twin hood doll's pram
with metal and wood body and leatherette
and fabric hood.   £50

1930's Pedigree pram by A. J. Dale & Son,
Warminster.   £55

Tan-Sad wartime Cot-Kar pram, No. 3214,
with wooden body and leatherette hood.
                                     £85

1930's simulated leather doll's pram with folding hood and brake. £35

1930's Stella doll's pram with plywood body, leatherette hood and umbrella holder. £40

An early Star Manufacturing Co. round-head pram with leather trim and porcelain handle. £250

Country style 'mail cart' push-chair with iron wheels. £100

A rare T. Trotmans patent 1854 folding pram with carpet back seating and wood and brass wheels. £400

The 'London' baby coach with wooden body and fabric cover. £55

PRAMS

Wooden 'mail cart' pram with carved sides,
leather hood and brass trim.   £300

Victorian wooden baby carriage, circa
1880, with slatted sides, 53in. long.
£250

1930's German wickerwork pram with alloy
wheel arches and bumpers.   £60

A wicker and bentwood baby carriage,
labelled Whitney, raised on wooden wheels
America, circa 1895, 55in. long.   £232

Victorian doll's wicker carriage, 29in. long,
circa 1890, in good condition.   £225

1920's Acme pram with wooden body and 'C
springs, reg. no. 465485.   £80

A 19th century carved and painted wood horse pull toy, mounted on wooden base with wheels, 11in. high.
£326

Late 19th/early 20th century painted walking gait wooden horse toy, America, mounted on an iron frame, 28in. long.
£460

Late 19th century hide covered horse pull toy, Germany, horse 24in. long, height on platform 27in.
£347

Edwardian plush model bear wheels, 1ft.4in. high, one and one eye missing. £100

An M. J. tinplate pull-along train, French, circa 1905, 11in. wide.
£240

German plush pull toy of a baby elephant by Steiff, 14in. overall.
£205

ate 19th century cast iron baby chick pull toy, patented 1881, 5in. high. £680

A honey plush covered pull-along bear on metal wheels, 6in. high, circa 1908, probably Steiff.
£286

Early 20th century goatskin goat pull toy, baa's when head is pressed down, Germany, 16½in. high.£530

RACING CARS

High quality metal model of the 100hp Sunbeam car which broke the world record in 1927. £750

An Alfa Romeo P2, by CIJ of France, circa 1926. £50[

A printed tinplate clockwork model of Sir M. Campbell's land speed record car 'Bluebird', circa 1930, 10¾in. long. £200

A Marklin tinplate clockwork constructo racing car, 1935, red, No. 7. £3[

Britains Bluebird, in original box. £160

A Bing hand-enamelled early two-seater Benz racing car, with steerable front wheels, Germa circa 1904, 11¼in. long. £9,2[

A Meccano racing constructor car with clockwork mechanism driving the rear axle, circa 1935, 11¾in. long. £350

A J.E.P. tinplate P.2 Alfa Romeo racing ca French, circa 1930, 20½in. long. £2[

RACING CARS

Gunthermann, Gordon Bennett clockwork racing car, finished in yellow with gold detail, 28cm. long. £4,000

A Marklin tinplate constructor racing car, German, circa 1935, 14¾in. long. £350

German clockwork racing car with original tyres. £90

A constructor Racing Car, probably French, with battery operated remote control, 29cm. long. £140

Y5 series 1, 1929 4½ litre Le Mans Bentley, in original box. £35

A painted tinplate model of a P2 Alfa Romeo racing car, with clockwork mechanism, by C.I.G., France, circa 1926, 21½in. long. £800

French Alfa-Romeo P2 clockwork tinplate racing car, circa 1935, 20½in. long. £660

An early Mettoy wind-up racing car. £75

ROBOTS

Television Spaceman, battery operated, moveable arms and legs, rotating eyes, screen in chest revealing a space scene, by Alps, Japanese, 1950's, 38.5cm. high: £508.

Planet Robot, battery operated with remote control, rotating antenna on top, with box, by Yoshiya, Japanese, 1950's, 23cm. high. £508

High Wheel Robot, clockwork mechanism, moveable legs, with visible rotating wheels, sparks in chest, with box, by Yoshiya (mk. 4), Japanese, 1960's, 25cm. high. £412

Gear Robot, battery operated, moveable legs with coloured wheel rotating chest and flashing head, possibly by Horikawa, Japanese, 1960's, 22.5cm. high. £333

Busy Cart Robot, battery operated, pushing and lifting a wheelbarrow, with box, by Horikawa (mk. 6), Japanese, 1960's/1970's, 30cm. high. £635

Ultraman, clockwork mechanism, moveable arms and legs, with box, by Bullmark (mk. 5), Japanese, 1960's, 23cm. high. £190

Attacking Martian, battery operated, moveable legs, chest opens to reveal flashing guns, with box, by Horikawa (mk. 6), Japanese, 1960's, 23cm. high. £540

Sparky Robot, clockwork mechanism, moveable legs and sparking eyes, with box, by Yoshiya, Japanese, 1950's, 19.5cm. high. £301

Answer-Game, battery operated, immobile, executes simple mathematics, flashing eyes, by Ichida (mk. 3), Japanese, 1960's, 35.5cm. high. £1,334

ROBOTS

Sparky Jim, battery operated with remote control, moveable legs and flashing eyes, Japanese, 1950's, 19.5cm. high. £667

Nando, the mechanism activated by air pressure through remote control, moveable legs and head, with box, by Opset, Italian, circa 1948, 13cm. high. £1,175

Astoman, clockwork mechanism, moveable arms and legs, by Nomura (mk. 1), Japanese, 1960's, 23.5cm. high. £571

Dyno Robot, battery operated, moveable legs, opening mask to reveal a flashing red dinosaur's head, with box, by Horikawa, Japanese, 1960's, 28.5cm. high. £412

Giant Robot, battery operated, moveable legs, chest opening to reveal flashing gun, possibly by Horikawa, Japanese, 1960's, 41cm. high. £635

Space Explorer, battery operated box transforms into Robot, revealing '3-D' television screen, with box, by Yonezawa (mk. 2), Japanese, 1960's, 29.5cm. high. £1,302

Talking Robot, battery powered, mobile, speaks four different messages, with box, by Yonezawa (mk. 2), Japanese, 1950's, 28cm. high. £825

Mr. Robot, clockwork mechanism and battery activated, with box, by Alps, Japanese, 1950's, 20cm. high. £857

Confectionary Dispenser, battery operated, with coinslot, transparent chest showing sweets, Italian, late 1960's, 139cm. high.£1,207

DOLLS & TOYS

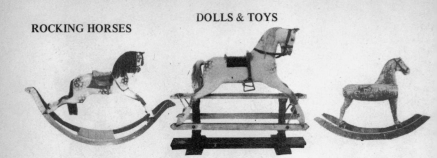

A Victorian carved wooden rocking horse. £500

A carved and painted rocking horse with hair mane and tail, America, circa 1880, 52in. long. £810

A carved and painted wooden rocking horse, probably English, circa 1720, 24½in. long. £300

A child's painted wooden rocking horse, probably Mass., with leather upholstered seat, 31in. high. £770

A carved and painted rocking horse with horsehair mane and tail, glass eyes and leather bridle and saddle, America, circa 1880, 72in. long. £1,635

A 19th century carved wood rocking horse, painted piebald with leather bridle, material covered saddle and grey horse hair tail, 7½ hands high. £1,045

A painted wood dapple grey 'pony size' rocking horse, with horse hair mane and tail, 56in. long, British. £350

A 20th century wooden rocking horse, painted black, leather bridle and saddle and mounted on a boat-shaped rocker base, 6ft.7in. long. £264

A large dappled rocking horse on metal hinged rockers, 51½in. high. £35

MPLERS

Boston 'Adam & Eve'
sampler by Lydia Hart,
May the 28, 1744, 9 x
11½in.   £24,665

A 17th century tent stitch panel
initialled A.M. and dated 1653,
1ft.9in. x 1ft.3in.   £1,760

A late 18th century
needlework sampler
by Jane Spurling,
1796, 16 x 12in.
£220

A needlework sampler
worked in silk and
wool threads, by Mary
Titchett, English,
1776, 17½ x 14½in.
£432

Spot motif sampler with
geometric panels in a variety
of stitches, circa 1630.
£1,500

An early 19th century needlework sampler by Selina
Doughty, 1835.   £280

sampler, 'Adam &
Eve', by Mary Simpson
Chamberlin, circa 1775,
9½ x 13¾in.   £2,702

A needlework sampler by Martha
Evans, English or American,
dated 1848, worked in polychrome wool yarns on an ivory
silk ground, 23½ x 27½in. £300

American early 19th century
framed needlework picture
worked on silk with chenille
silk, wool yarns, 16¼ x 16½in.
£135

221

A sampler by Mary-Ann Hayter, aged 8 years, 1823, worked in coloured silks, 15 x 13in. £340

Early 19th century woolwork sampler, worked by Elizabeth Shufflebottoms 1841, 23½ x 23¾in. £300

An early 19th century American needlework sampler, 19? x 21in. £1,90?

A sampler by Julia Matild Paisey, 1845, worked in dark silks, 16 x 12½in. £520

A George IV needlework sampler, by E.H., 1826, 17 x 12½in. £340

A needlework sampler by Mar? Anne Hunter aged 14 years 1844, 26 x 16½in. £32?

Needlework sampler, marked 'Elizabeth C. Engle's work done in the 12th year of her age, August 23th, 1837', 17½ x 17½in. £416

An American needlework sampler, signed Jane Littlefield, circa 1810, worked in silk threads on a dark green canvas, 24in. high, 15½in. wide. £2,729

An early 19th century needlework sampler, 'Hannah L. Slessor aged 13 years', New England, 16½ x 15½in. £590

A needlework sampler, 'Emily urber her sampler aged 10, wrought March 16, 1827', 23 x 26in.   £1,666

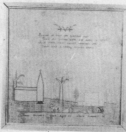

An early 19th century needlework sampler, 'Jane Slessors work aged 13 years January 16', New England, 17 x 17½in.   £347

Needlework sampler marked 'Wrought by Sally Alden June 14 1811', Mass., 16 x 21in.   £2,604

A needlework family register worked by Lucia A. Daniels 1832, 16 x 18in.   £694

An 18th century needlework sampler well decorated in coloured silks, 17 x 12½in.   £520

A sampler by Charlotte Way, Portland, 1841, worked in pale brown silk, 14 x 11½in.   £140

A needlework sampler, 'Anna owler born March 2, 1739, is sampler I did the year 54', 13 x 19½in. £1,597

Early 19th century needlework sampler, 'Phebe L. Slessor work aged 11 years', New England, 16 x 16in.   £625

Late 18th century needlework sampler family record, 10½ x 16in.   £2,152

223

SAMPLERS

Needlework sampler, silk yarns worked on ivory linen ground fabric, by 'Harriatt Shoveller, 1799', England, 12½ x 17in. £1,118

Framed needlework pictorial sampler, inscribed 'Harroit Hoyle, Aged 21, 1834', 24 x 24in. £1,538

Needlework spot sample Germany, 1759, vivid polychrome silk yarns o natural linen fabric, 12 x 21½in. £1,74

Needlework sampler, 'Sally Butman her work in the 11th year of her age, 1801', Marble-head, Mass., 10.3/8 x 12½in. £10,489

Needlework sampler, England, dated 1826, silk yarns in a variety of stitches on natural linen ground, 13 x 15½in. £489

A needlework picture, b Mary Fentun, dated 178 21¼ x 16½in. £2,00

An early 19th century needle-work sampler by S. Parker, aged 14 years 1817, 37 x 32cm. £560

An early 19th century needle-work sampler, by Elizabeth Campling, aged 12 years, the linen ground embroidered in silks, 31.5 x 34.5cm. £220

A nicely worked needlework sampler, by Sarah Iesson, the linen ground embroidered in silks, 33 x 21cm. £460

e 18th century needlework
pler, worked in silk yarns
old, light blue, red, brown,
y and black on natural
n, 7 x 10½in.   £2,307

A needlework sampler worked
in silk yarns on natural
coloured linen, 'Susanah
Cadmore, 1805', 12½ x 13¼in.
       £349

An early 19th century needlework sampler, inscribed 'Rachel
Fowler's work finished May 29,
1837', 40 x 32cm.   £480

e 18th century Spanish
dlework sampler with silk
broidered stylised floral
geometric designs, 15½
8½in.   £209

A needlework family record,
silk yarns in shades of blue,
green, pale peach, ivory and
black on natural linen ground
fabric, 18¼ x 14½in.   £629

A needlwork sampler, by
'Sarah Pell, Febrery 21, 1830',
wool yarns on white wool
fabric, 12½ x 16in.   £594

early 19th century needle-
k sampler by Elizabeth
hby, March 6, aged 10
rs, 1822, 45 x 42cm.
       £340

Framed needlework pictorial
verse sampler, by Eliza. A.
Machett, New York, March
22, 1828, 16½ x 16in. £333

Needlework sampler, by
'Elizabeth Tonnecliff, her
work done in 1791', silk
yarns, 16 x 20¼in.
       £6,083

DOLLS & TOYS

SAMPLERS

A mid 17th century needlework sampler in drawnthread, cutwork and needlepoint stitches, 75 x 22.5cm.   £750

An 18th century silk embroidered sampler, Europe, 20 x 35in. £5,244

A 17th century needlework sampler, probably by Mary Tratt of Boston, 7½ x 22¾in £1,74

A framed pictorial needlework sampler, inscribed 'Celia(?) Procter Montrose 1833', England, 16 x 20in.   £297

A late 17th century needlework sampler, embroidered in silks, 36 x 14cm.   £290

A framed pictorial needlework sampler, inscribed 'Mary Jagger 1807', England, 17¼ x 19½in.   £192

Late 19th century Bidjar sampler, N.W. Persia, 3ft. 10in. x 4ft.11in. £3,125

A framed needlework verse sampler, 'Rebecca Miers', New England, circa 1830, 22 x 21in.   £466

Needlework sampler, Engla 'Margaret Smith, aged 12 A 1848', worked in heavy wo yarns, 17 x 18in.   £4

Mid 18th century Boston
chool, Adam & Eve sam-
ler, 6¾ x 11½in. £5,384

Sampler by Ann Foss of
Houghton, Le Spring, 1813,
12½ x 17in. £420

Mid 19th century wool
worked picture of a
mother and child.£200

rly 19th century Adam and
e sampler by Eliz. Tredick,
w Hampshire or Southern
ine, 11 x 16in. £1,270

Mid 18th century Boston School
needlework picture of a shep-
herdess and piper in a landscape,
19 x 14in. £50,000

A needlework sampler
made by Sarah Johnson,
Newport, Rhode Island,
1769, 9 x 16in. £16,279

Georgian needlework
ampler by Maria Coster,
the tenth year of her age,
19, 1ft.5in. x 1ft.1in.
£660

A Boston School needlework
sampler, made by Sarah
Henderson in 1765, aged 12,
21 x 18½in. £15,384

A needlework sampler by Susanna
H. White, Marblehead, dated 1806,
14½ x 19in. £11,110

A needlework sampler, 'Sina Halls Sampler Wrought at Wallingford, August 10, 1811', worked in a variety of stitches on moss-green linsey-woolsey ground, 15¾ x 17½in. £8,333

A sampler 'Wrought by Harriot Wethrell May Aged 10 years, Plymouth Massachusetts, June 10th 1830', 16¼ x 16½in. £1,130

A mid 19th century Armenian needlework sampler by Souepi Kedeasian, the linen ground embroidered in red and pink threads, 45 x 58cm. £90

A needlework sampler by Eliz. Matilda Whitcombe aged 11, 1846, embroidered in coloured silks on a wool ground, 43 x 32cm. £320

Needlework sampler, 'Rhoda Roger's Sampler wrought in the 11 years of her age 1804', Mass. £3,370

A mid 19th century needlework sampler by Sarah Redfern, 1.04 x 0.77m., framed and glazed. £500

Needlework picture, entitled 'The Beggar's Petition', by Sarah Hadley, 1841, 24 x 24in. £1,573

An 18th century sampler, by Kezi Ladell, July 11, 1799, 37 x 21cm. £200

A needlework family register, 'Wrought by Hannah Winchell, 1822', 22½ x 23½in. £1,547

A needlework picture, signed Anne Oram and dated 1824, worked in polychrome threads on natural ground, 10 x 12in. £248

An early 18th century needlework sampler, the linen ground embroidered in coloured silks, 46 x 21cm. £850

A needlework sampler made by 'Anna Braddock . . . A work wrought in the 14th year of her age, 1826', 22½ x 26in. £22,619

Late 18th century framed needlework sampler, by Charlotte Richardson 13 years, Dec. 1786, American, 17 x 20in. £937

A needlework sampler 'Susannah Styles finished this work in the 10 years of her age 1800', worked in silk yarns on wool ground, 13in. square. £595

Sampler with alphabet verse and figures of plants and birds, dated 1824, 17 x 13in. £300

A needlework sampler by Mary Ann Cash, 1801, the linen ground worked in coloured silks, 37 x 30cm. £200

A 17th century needlwork sampler by Anna Stone, the linen ground worked in pink, green and blue silk threads, 41 x 19cm. £700

Needlework sampler, 'Betsey Stevens, her sampler wrought in 10th year of her age AD 1796', silk yarns on linen, 15 x 16in. £1,685

DOLLS & TOYS

A William IV needle-work sampler by Mary Belt, 1833, 1ft. 11½in. x 1ft. 9in. **£935**

Early 19th century unfinished Shaker needle-work sampler on natural linen, 8½ x 10¼in. **£440**

An American needle-work sampler by Maria Alligood, 1802, 26¼ x 21¼in. **£1,600**

'Life of a Man' needlework sampler, early 19th century, American. **£4,000**

A fine spot motif sampler, the ivory linen ground with geometric samples, circa 1630. **£2,000**

A needlework sampler by Catherine Lewis, Wales, 1867, worked in polychrome wool yarns, 52 x 28in. **£235**

An embroidered band sampler by Elizabeth Woodworth, 1758. **£750**

A needlework sampler worked in silk and wool threads on a linen ground, by Hannah S. Pidgeon, 1813, 17½ x 25¾in. **£1,885**

A sampler by Emma Toogood finished June 28th, early 19th century. **£300**

Girl with Plum Pudding,
2½in. high.   £1.50

Miss Jenny Wren and Mr Riah.
£5

Little Dorrit and her Lover,
John Chivery.   £5

Mr Dick and Betsy Trotwood.
£5

Victoria Cross Gallery, Sergeant
H. Ramage.   £5

The Lucky Clown, 12in.
high.   £7.50

Agnes Wickfield and Uriah
Heep.   £5

Girl in Blue Gown, 5in.
high.   £2

Dick Swiveller and The Mar-
chioness.   £5

SCRAPS

Girl in a Feathered Hat,
4in. high.   £1.50

Winged Cherub, 4in. wide. £4

Girl in a Green
Dress, 4in. high.
£1.50

Girl with a Songbird,
3½in. high.   £1.50

Kitten in a Floral Basket, 9in.
high.   £7

The 17th Lancers,
4in. high.   £1

H.R.H. The Duchess
of York.   £3

Girl in a Bonnet,
4in. high.   £1.50

H.M.G.M. The Queen in 1937,
10in. high.   £7.50

1st Bengal Cavalry,
4in. high.   £1

Romeo and Juliet,
2½in. high.   £1.50

Eggs in the Nest,
1in. high.   75p

Rabbit in the Grass, 2in. wide.
£1

Pansies, 2in. high.
25p

Schoolgirl Feeding
Birds, 2in. high. 75p

1930's Boy with
Flowers, 3in. high.
75p

An Oak Tree, 9in. high. £3

Girl with Clown Doll,
3in. high.   £3

Cherub on a Cloud.
75p

H.R.H. The Princess
of Wales.   £3

H.M.G.M. The Queen in 1897,
10in. high.   £6

Girl in Pink, 5in. high.
£2

'O' was an Organman, 'P' was a Parson, 6in. high.   £5

Forget-me-nots, 3½in. high.   £1.50

The King and The Lady.   £5

'S' was a Sailor, 'T' was a Tinker.   £5

Red Roses, 3½in. high.   £3

Tom Pinch and his sister Ruth.   £5

'M' was a Miser, 'N' was a Nobleman.   £5

Love Birds, 3in. high.   £1

'U' was an Usher, 'V' was a Veteran, 'W' was a Watchman, 'X' was Expensive. £5

'G' was a Gamester, 'H' was
a Hunter.   £5

Peasant Girl with Dove,
4½in. high.   £2

'Y' was a Youth, 'Z' was
a Zany.   £5

'C' was a Captain, 'D' was a
Drummer.   £5

Rose in Hand, 7in. high.
       £3

Mr Serjeant Buzfuz, Mrs
Bardell and Master Tommy
Bardell.   £5

'I' was an Italian, 'J' was a
Joiner.   £5

Love Birds on the Bough,
3in. high.   £1

'E' was an Earl, 'F' was a
Farmer.   £5

Cupid with Arrow, 3½in. high. £1

Newman Noggs and Nicholas Nickleby's Children. £5

Gabriel Varden and Sim Tappertit. £5

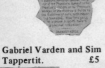

Victoria Cross Gallery, Serg't. Joseph Malone. £5

Father Christmas with Presents. £2.50

Mr Tupman, Miss Wardle and the Fat Boy. £5

Old Mr Turveydrop and Peepy and Guppy. £5

Girl in Red Dress, 5in. high. £2

Joe Gargery and Pip. £5

SKITTLES

The ABC nine-pin and spelling blocks by McLoughlin Bros., New York, 1870-80. £100

A 17th century wooden skittle doll carved as a puritan woman, 6in. high. £200

A Harlequin set of nine Steiff skittles, circa 1908, on circular wooden bases. £4,840

Six turned polychrome Ring Toss Game figures, New England, late 19th century, 14½in. high. £1,825

A group of felt-covered animal skittles, complete with two balls, the largest 11in. high, circa 1910. £350

SOFT TOYS

Miniature cloth bear on wheels, circa 1900, 5 x 3in., with glass button eyes. **£100**

French 'walking pussy cat' toy with white fur covering, circa 1930, 30cm. long. **£150**

Late 19th/early 20th century fur-covered papier mache polar bear, 16½in. long.**£250**

A clockwork fur covered giraffe with clown rider, 31cm. high, and an HK, Fipps, clockwork nodding puppy. **£55**

Italian cloth comic figure in tan felt, by Lenci Torino, circa 1955, 11in. high. **£150**

Mid 20th century life-size young donkey, probably Steiff, 39in. high, 39in. long. **£120**

A walking Felix the cat soft toy, circa 1928, 33½in. long. **£1,210**

A 'Nora Wellings' pre-war fur fabric monkey, 11½in. high. **£36**

Felix the cat with toothy grin, circa 1928, 16in. high. **£750**

1960's Japanese flying saucer with robot operator. £20

A Marx Buck Rogers spaceship, Pat. 1927, lithographed tin, 12in. long. £250

TM, battery operated Supersonic Moon Ship, boxed. £110

Japanese made 1960's flying saucer, X15, complete with robot operator. £20

SH-Japanese battery operated Space Station, boxed. £270

Karl Bub, clockwork Atom Rocket Ship, boxed. £110

'Space Explorer', Hong Kong plastic battery operated 1960's robot. £25

1960's Japanese space explorer vehicle with robot operator. £20

STATIONS

A Marklin hand painted tinplate Central Station, circa 1904.   £10,000

Two No. 116 Ives Union Stations, together with platform cover, circa 1928.   £1,233

1930's wooden railway booking office, Brighton & South Coast Railway.   £18

A printed tinplate station, by Carette, circa 1912.   £220

An early Marklin gauge 1 mainline station, hand-enamelled, fitted for candle lighting, circa 1903.   £660

Fine electric hand built working model railway exhibition display, circa 1947, 12ft. x 15ft. 6in.   £1,800

EDDY BEARS

Steiff Centennial teddy
ear, for the German market,
lden mohair, black button
ves and ear button, 17in.
gh, 1980. £269

Blonde mohair jointed teddy
bear, 1910, 17in. high. £190

An R.D. France drinking bear,
dark brown and white rabbit
fur, glass eyes, electrical,
1930's, 14½in. high. £461

tan mohair bear with wired
mbs, blonde plush ears,
out and feet and glass eyes,
ermany, circa 1930, 11in.
gh. £38

An early gold plush tumbling
teddy bear, the body of wood
and cardboard, containing a
key-wind mechanism, 9in.
high. £55

A Steiff blonde plush teddy
bear, with metal disc in left
ear, 17in. high. £990

wo early 20th century
inted teddy bears, one with
onde mohair, 19in. high,
e other yellow mohair,
½in. high. £243

A golden plush-covered musical teddy bear, playing
Sonny Boy by Al Jolson,
20in. high, circa 1930. £550

A plush-covered teddy bear
with round ears, button
eyes, pronounced hump and
long paws, probably by
Steiff, 21in. high. £300

TEDDY BEARS

Pre-war fur fabric teddy bear, 15in. high. £20

A Steiff pale plush teddy bear with black thread stitched nose and straw stuffed body, with button in left ear, 33cm. high. £500

Early amber plush teddy bear and accessories, circ 1910, 15in. tall. £12

A gold short plush covered teddy bear, slight hump, 15½in. high, circa 1926. £187

A golden plush covered teddy bear in the form of a child's muff, 15in. high. £176

A gold plush teddy bear, wi metal Steiff disc in left ear, German, circa 1907, 25in. high. £2,00

A golden plush covered teddy bear with pronounced hump, pointed snout and with Steiff button in ear, 29in. high. £2,860

A dark plush teddy bear with straw stuffed body and elongated arms, back hump and felt pads, probably by Steiff, 40cm. high. £420

An orange plush teddy bear with smiling mouth, small hump back and swive joints, 16in. high, circa 1930. £8

te 19th century clock-
rk brown bear, real fur
t, possibly France, 7in.
h.   £114

Tan mohair teddy bear
with shoe button eyes,
circa 1910, 12¾in. high.
                    £133

A musical teddy bear with
swivelling head operated via
his tail, 43cm. high. £200

clockwork somersaulting
dy bear dressing in gold
t jacket, blue trouser and
ite vest, by Bing of
remberg, 9in. high. £572

Two teddy bears, one
14in. high, the other 8¼in.
high, German, circa 1930.
                    £187

A golden plush covered teddy
bear with boot button eyes,
cut muzzle, hump and elongated limbs, with Steiff button in left ear, 19in. high.
                    £528

londe mohair plush
dy bear with voice box,
a 1910, 18½in. high.
                    £264

German straw-filled teddy
bear with hump back, pad
feet, long nose and button
eyes, 11in. high.   £190

A pale golden plush covered
teddy bear with embroidered
snout and slight hump,
15½in. high, with Steiff
button.   £935

TEDDY BEARS

Early white mohair teddy bear, Germany, circa 1906, 13½in. high. £533

German teddy bear by Steiss of pale plush colour, renewed pads, snout and nose, circa 1909. £1,100

A dark plush teddy bear with wide apart rounded ears, black button eyes and pointed snout probably by Steiff, 34cm. high £40

A dual-coloured teddy bear, with black and beige tufted mohair plush, circa 1950, 25in. high. £22

A long plush-covered teddy bear with black button eyes, with Steiff button in the ear, 25in. high. £1,300

A teddy bear of grey plush with brown button eyes, embroidered nose, hump back and long paws, 13in. high. £3

A chubby long blonde mohair teddy bear, fully jointed with glass eyes, 20in. high. £134

A golden plush covered teddy bear, the front unhooking to reveal a metal hot water bottle, by Steiff, 17in. high. £1,100

A straw filled ginger teddy bear, with ball and socket joints, 74cm. high. £

TINPLATE TOYS

A 70mm. scale figure of the Colonel-in-Chief, the Welsh Guards, with painted legend 'South Africa 1947' on the base, in original box, Britain's. £1,200

Max lithographed tin Amos and Andy, N.Y., 1930, 11½in. high. £451

A German made tinplate sentry box with 60mm. mounted sentry of The Royal Horse Guards, in original box, 1890. £330

A Marklin tinplate 'Rocket' gauge 1 train set, German, circa 1909. £28,050

German made, a tinplate sentry box with 120mm. Sentry of the Foot Guards, in original box, 1890. £260

Early 20th century embossed die cut Santa sleigh with reindeer, Germany, 15¾in. long. £138

A painted metal model lighthouse with winding staircase on exterior, electrified, 40in. high. £155

245

TRACTION ENGINES

An exhibition standard 2in. scale model of a
Burrell 5 N.H.P. double crank compound
three shaft, two speed Showman's Road
Locomotive, 20 x 30½in.   £5,500

A 3in. scale model of a single cylinder two
speed, four shaft Clayton & Shuttleworth
traction engine, built by K. Prout, 31 x 56in.
                                £2,800

A well engineered 2in. scale model of an
Aveling and Porter twin crank compound
two speed, four shaft Road Roller, 19½
x 35in.   £2,600

A 3in. scale live steam coal-fired Burrell
single-cylinder agricultural traction engine
'Myrtle', by Dennis Hurn, 45in. long
overall.   £2,200

An exhibition standard 1½in. scale model of
the Allchin single cylinder two-speed four-
shaft General Purpose Traction Engine (Royal
Chester).   £1,500

A 2in. scale model of a single cylinder three
shaft two speed Davey-Paxman general purpose agricultural traction engine built by A.
R. Dyer & Sons, Wantage, 23½ x 38in.£1,800

A 4½in. scale model of a Burrell single cylinder, two-speed, three-shaft general purpose traction engine, built by Lion Engineering Co., 1971, length of engine 68in. £4,000

A sturdily constructed 2in. scale model of a Fowler twin crank compound three speed, four shaft road locomotive built by S. W. Brown, Newbury, 23 x 37in. £2,400

A finely engineered, exhibition standard 1in. scale model of the single cylinder two speed four shaft general purpose agricultural traction engine 'Doreen', built to the designs of 'Minnie', by H. A. Taylor, 1980, 11½ x 18in. £1,100

An exhibition standard 2in. scale model of the Burrell 5 n.h.p. double crank compound two speed three shaft 'Gold Medal' tractor, engine No. 3846, Registration No. AD7782 'Poussnouk-nouk', built from works drawings by P. Penn-Sayers, Laughton, 19¾ x 27¼in. £7,500

A 1½in. scale model of a Burrell single crank compound two speed three shaft general purpose agricultural traction engine, built by J. B. Harris, Solihull, 15½ x 25in. £2,200

A tinplate model of a fair-ground traction engine, with a four-wheeled car containing a carousel, by Bing, circa 1906. £480

VANS & TRUCKS

Spot-On, 265 Tonibell Ice Cream van, with
server, in original box.   **£50**

A tinplate Lineol ambulance, No. WH 2517,
German, circa 1938, 12in. long.   **£396**

Dinky 28M green delivery van advertising
'Atco Motor Mowers'.   **£280**

Dinky Supertoys, 919 Guy van, advertising
'Golden Shred', in original paintwork, with
golly, in original box.   **£440**

A Wells tinplate ambulance, clockwork
mechanism driving rear axle, 6½in. long,
English, circa 1935.   **£143**

Spot-On — 110 2B A.E.C. Major Brick Lorry
(E to M), boxed.   **£180**

Tekno, Mercedes Tuborg Pilsner Delivery
lorry, boxed.   **£60**

Buddy L sheet metal railway express truck,
green cab and open hauler, circa 1950, 21in.
long.   **£100**

NS & TRUCKS

ky Supertoys, 514B Guy Van, advertising
ons Swiss Rolls', in original paintwork and
k. £352

Pre-war yellow-bodied Dinky delivery van,
advertising Kodak film. £450

nky 28/3a Hornby Trains Delivery Van,
nished in red, advertising 'Hornby Trains
itish and Guaranteed', in gold decals.£220

Dinky model Guy van, 'Weetabix', No. 514,
boxed. £460

Inky Guy 'Spratts' van, no. 514, boxed.
£200

A Dinky Series 28 first pattern delivery van,
painted in black and red with gilt decals,
'The Manchester Guardian', circa 1935. £240

Inky series 25D petrol tanker, 4½in. long,
glish, circa 1939. £150

Dinky van advertising Pickfords. £340

VANS & TRUCKS

Early 20th century child's toy pick-up truck painted black.   £66

A Britains Army Ambulance, with driver, in original box.   £100

A Dinky model Guy van with upright radiator grill, unboxed.   £42

A searchlight lorry with adjustable electric searchlight, in the original box.   £190

Dinky van advertising Oxo.   £250

Dinky Supertoy, No. 514C Guy van, advertising 'Weetabix', in original paintwork and box.
£286

Spot-On, 271 Express Dairy van, with driver and milk crates, in original box.   £30

A boxed set of six green and cream Tipper lorries with drivers.   £200

'Dinky van advertising The Manchester Guardian.   £340

A Distler lorry and trailer with clockwork mechanism driving the rear
axle, German, circa 1935, 19¾in. long.
£418

nic pre-war No. 30M 'Minic Transport'
tic, in original paintwork, with transfers,
trol can and white rubber tyres.   £55

A Chad Valley games van with clockwork
mechanism, English, circa 1930.   £121

2in. scale model of a Garrett 'undertype
ee-way tipper, live-steam wagon, 30in. long.
£1,020

Spot-On — 110/4 4000 gallon Auto Petrol
Tanker (M), boxed.   £400

mann tinplate postal delivery van, No. 786,
rman, circa 1927, 7¼in. long.   £605

Dinky van advertising Hornby trains. £340

WOODEN TOYS

American six-piece carved wooden polar bear with socket head, by Schoenhut of Philadelphia.
£140

Mid 19th century child's wooden velocipede, probably New York State, 31in. long.
£220

Six-piece carved wooden leopa by Schoenhut of Philadelphia, 7in.
£1

'Our New Clergyman', a stained and carved wood, metal and tinplate preacher, probably by F. Martin, circa 1890, 10½in. high.
£1,540

American carved wooden five-piece goose, with two-part articulated head and throat, by Schoenhut of Philadelphia.
£200

Rare early 18th century wood model of a hand knitting fram 6in. high.
£1,000

Late 19th century Folk Art painted and carved mechanised wooden model of five bearded men at work, America, base 18½in. long.
£714

A carved and painted wooden zebra carousel figure, attributed to H. Speilman, circa 1880, 33in. high.
£2,361

A carved wooden paddle t modelled as a peacock, 9½ high.
£

INDEX